# It's another Quality Book from CGP

This book is for anyone doing Edexcel Modular
GCSE Mathematics at Higher Level.

Whatever subject you're doing it's the same
old story — there are lots of facts and you've just got
to learn them.  KS4 Maths is no different.

Happily this CGP book gives you all that important
information as clearly and concisely as possible.

It's also got some daft bits in to try and make the whole
experience at least vaguely entertaining for you.

# What CGP is all about

Our sole aim here at CGP is to produce the highest quality
books — carefully written, immaculately presented and
dangerously close to being funny.

Then we work our socks off to get them out to you
— at the cheapest possible prices.

Published by CGP

Written by Richard Parsons

Updated by: Rosie Gillham, Neil Hastings, Helena Hayes, Simon Little, Julie Wakeling, Janet West, Sarah Williams

Proofreading by: Vicky Daniel, Sharon Keeley

ISBN: 978 1 84762 093 4

Groovy website: www.cgpbooks.co.uk
Printed by Elanders Ltd, Newcastle upon Tyne.
Jolly bits of clipart from CorelDRAW®

# Contents

# Calculating Tips

Ah, the glorious world of GCSE Maths.  Ok — maybe it's more like wiffy socks at times, but learn it you must.
Edexcel Modular Maths is split into 3 units, each with their own exam — yuk.  Thankfully there are some nifty
exam tricks you only have to learn once, which could get you marks in all 3 exams.  Read on...

## BODMAS     Brackets, Other, Division, Multiplication, Addition, Subtraction

<u>BODMAS</u> tells you the <u>ORDER</u> in which these operations should be done:
Work out <u>Brackets</u> first, then <u>Other</u> things like squaring, then <u>Divide</u> / <u>Multiply</u>
groups of numbers before <u>Adding</u> or <u>Subtracting</u> them.

This set of rules works really well, so remember the word BODMAS.

**Example:**     A mysterious quantity T, is given by:  $T = (P - 7)^2 + 4R/Q$
Find the value of T when P = 4, Q = -2 and R = 3

| | | | |
|---|---|---|---|
| Write down the formula: | $T$ | $= (P - 7)^2 + 4R/Q$ | |
| Put the numbers in: | $T$ | $= (4 - 7)^2 + 4\times3/\text{-}2$ | |
| Then work it out <u>in stages</u>: | | $= (-3)^2 + 4\times3/\text{-}2$ | |
| | | $= 9 + 4\times3/\text{-}2$ | |
| | | $= 9 + \text{-}6$ | |
| | | $= 9 - 6 = \underline{3}$ | |

<u>Note BODMAS in operation:</u>
<u>Brackets</u> worked out
first, then <u>squared</u>.
<u>Multiplications</u> and <u>divisions</u>
done <u>before</u> finally <u>adding</u>
and <u>subtracting</u>.

## Always Check Your Answer

It's always a good idea to <u>check</u>
your answers by working <u>backwards</u>
through your calculations.

That way you can pick up any <u>silly</u>
<u>mistakes</u> you might have made.

**Example:**     If $y = 2x^2 + 3$, find the value of y when x = 3.

<u>Answer:</u>  $y = 2 \times (3)^2 + 3$       <u>Check:</u>  $21 - 3 = 18$
$\phantom{y} = 2 \times 9 + 3$
$\phantom{y} = 18 + 3$              $18 \div 2 = 9$
$\phantom{y} = \underline{21}$                    $\sqrt{9} = 3$

Hurray — you've got
the same number you
started with.

## Don't Be Scared of Wordy Questions

About <u>a quarter</u> of the marks on your exam are for answering <u>wordy</u>, <u>real-life</u> questions.  For these
you don't just have to do <u>the maths</u>, you've got to work out what the question's <u>asking you to do</u>.
<u>Relax</u> and work through them <u>step by step</u>.

1) <u>READ</u> the question <u>carefully</u>.  Work out <u>what bit of maths</u> you need to answer it.

2) <u>Underline</u> the <u>INFORMATION YOU NEED</u> to answer the question — you might not
have to use <u>all</u> the numbers they give you.

3) Write out the question <u>IN MATHS</u> and answer it, showing all your <u>working</u> clearly.

**Example:**

a)  The table shows rates of <u>depreciation</u> over a three year period for three
different motorbikes.  Helen bought a B260 for £6300 three years ago.
How much is the motorbike worth now?

| Model | Depreciation over 3 years |
|---|---|
| A125 | 37% |
| B260 | <u>45%</u> |
| F400 | 42% |

1) The word "<u>depreciation</u>" tells you this is a <u>percentages</u> question.

2) You need the initial value of <u>£6300</u> and the B260 depreciation of <u>45%</u>.

The rest of the table
is irrelevant.

3) "Depreciation" is a <u>percentage decrease</u>, so in maths:
$£6300 \times (1 - 0.45) = \underline{£3465}$

Don't forget to include any <u>units</u>.

Percentage questions are covered on pages 4, 5 and 69.

# Calculating Tips

You're allowed to use a calculator in the exams for Units 1 and 3 — hurray! Make sure you know how your shiny grey friend can help you, and watch the marks roll in. Here's just a few things you'll end up using all the time.

## BODMAS and the BRACKETS BUTTONS ( and )

1) This is really important when you want to work out even a simple thing like $\frac{23 + 45}{64 \times 3}$.

2) You can't just press [23] [+] [45] [÷] [64] [×] [3] [=] — it will be completely wrong.

3) The calculator follows BODMAS, so it'll think you mean $23 + \frac{45}{64} \times 3$.

4) The secret is to OVERRIDE the automatic BODMAS order of operations using the BRACKETS BUTTONS. Anything in brackets is worked out before anything else happens to it.

5) So all you have to do is write a couple of pairs of brackets into the expression like this: $\frac{(23 + 45)}{(64 \times 3)}$

6) Then just type it as it's written: [(] [23] [+] [45] [)] [÷] [(] [64] [×] [3] [)] [=]

It's OK to have brackets within other brackets too, e.g. (4 + (5÷2)). As a rule, you can't cause trouble by putting too many brackets in... **SO LONG AS THEY ALWAYS GO IN PAIRS.**

## The Fraction Button: [a b/c]

Use this as much as possible in the calculator papers. It's very easy and dead useful.

1) To enter $\frac{1}{4}$ press [1] [a b/c] [4]

2) To enter $1\frac{3}{5}$ press [1] [a b/c] [3] [a b/c] [5]

3) To work out $\frac{1}{5} \times \frac{3}{4}$ press [1] [a b/c] [5] [×] [3] [a b/c] [4] [=]

4) To reduce a fraction to its lowest terms enter it and press [=] e.g. $\frac{9}{12}$ — [9] [a b/c] [12] [=] [ 3⌐4 ] = $\frac{3}{4}$

5) To convert between mixed and top-heavy fractions press [SHIFT] [a b/c]. E.g. $2\frac{3}{8}$ — [2] [a b/c] [3] [a b/c] [8] [=] [SHIFT] [a b/c] which gives $\frac{19}{8}$

## The MEMORY BUTTONS ([STO] Store, [RCL] Recall)

These are really useful for keeping a number you've just calculated, so you can use it again shortly afterwards.

E.g. Find $\frac{840}{15 + 12\sin 40}$ — just work out the bottom line first and stick it in the memory.

So press [15] [+] [12] [SIN] [40] [=] and then [STO] [M] to keep the result of the bottom line in the memory. Then you simply press [840] [÷] [RCL] [M] [=], and the answer is 36.98.

> The memory buttons might work a bit differently on your calculator. Note, if your calculator has an 'Ans' button, you can do the same thing — the Ans button gives you the result you got when you last pressed the '=' button.

## Make Sure You Know What Your Answer Means

It's taken 2 minutes of frenzied button pressing and finally your calculator screen looks like this. Before you merrily jot down 3.6 as your answer, think about what it means — 3.6 what? [ 3.6 ] Pipers piping? It sounds silly, but it can lose you easy marks in the exam. E.g. If you're answering a money question, 3.6 won't get you any marks — you'll probably need to write £3.60.

## Learn these two pages, store, then recall...

Learn this stuff — it can really help you rack up marks whichever exam you're doing. Right, on with the rest of the show. Laaaaaaaadies and gentlemeeeeeeen — I give you, the one, the only — Edexcel Maths G C S Eeee.

# Fractions, Decimals and Percentages

The one word that could describe all these three is <u>PROPORTION</u>.  Fractions, decimals and percentages are simply <u>three different ways</u> of expressing a <u>proportion</u> of something — and it's pretty important you should see them as <u>closely related and completely interchangeable</u> with each other.  This table shows the really common conversions which you should know straight off without having to work them out:

| Fraction | Decimal | Percentage |
|:---:|:---:|:---:|
| $\frac{1}{2}$ | 0.5 | 50% |
| $\frac{1}{4}$ | 0.25 | 25% |
| $\frac{3}{4}$ | 0.75 | 75% |
| $\frac{1}{3}$ | 0.333333... | 33% |
| $\frac{2}{3}$ | 0.666666... | 67% |
| $\frac{1}{10}$ | 0.1 | 10% |
| $\frac{2}{10}$ | 0.2 | 20% |
| $\frac{X}{10}$ | 0.X | X0% |
| $\frac{1}{5}$ | 0.2 | 20% |
| $\frac{2}{5}$ | 0.4 | 40% |

*See page 3 for tips on handling fractions with your calculator.*

*It's usually easiest to compare or order fractions by changing them all to decimals — easy peasy on your calculator...*

The more of those conversions you learn, the better — but for those that you <u>don't know</u>, you must <u>also learn</u> how to <u>convert</u> between the three types.  These are the methods:

**Fraction** $\xrightarrow{\substack{\text{Divide (use your}\\\text{calculator if you can)}}}$ **Decimal** $\xrightarrow{\times \text{ by 100}}$ **Percentage**

e.g. $\frac{1}{2}$ is $1 \div 2$     = 0.5     e.g. $0.5 \times 100$     = 50%

**Fraction** $\xleftarrow{\text{The awkward one}}$ **Decimal** $\xleftarrow{\div \text{ by 100}}$ **Percentage**

<u>Converting decimals to fractions</u> is fairly easy to do when you have <u>exact</u> (terminating) decimals.  It's best illustrated by examples — you should be able to work out the rule...

$0.6 = \frac{6}{10}$    $0.3 = \frac{3}{10}$    $0.7 = \frac{7}{10}$    $0.x = \frac{x}{10}$ etc.

$0.12 = \frac{12}{100}$    $0.78 = \frac{78}{100}$    $0.45 = \frac{45}{100}$    $0.05 = \frac{5}{100}$ etc.

$0.345 = \frac{345}{1000}$    $0.908 = \frac{908}{1000}$    $0.024 = \frac{24}{1000}$    $0.xyz = \frac{xyz}{1000}$ etc.

*These can then be <u>cancelled down</u> using your calculator — see p.3*

Scary-looking <u>recurring</u> decimals like 0.3333333 are actually just <u>exact fractions</u> in disguise.  There is a simple method for converting them into fractions — see page 45...

## Fractions — they're like recurring nightmares...

<u>Learn</u> the whole of the top table and the 4 conversion processes.  Then it's time to break into a mild sweat...

1) Turn the following decimals into fractions and reduce them to their simplest form.
    a) 0.6    b) 0.02    c) 0.77    d) 0.555    e) 5.6

# Percentages

You shouldn't have any trouble with most percentage questions, especially types 1 and 2.

**Type 1**  "Find x% of y" — e.g. Find 15% of £46 ⇒ 0.15 × 46 = £6.90

**Type 2**  "Express x as a percentage of y"
e.g. Give 40p as a percentage of £3.34 ⇒ (40 ÷ 334) × 100 = 12%

**Type 3**  "Find the new value when y decreases by x%"
e.g. A shirt is on sale for 20% off the original price.
If the original price was £30, how much is it in the sale?
A decrease of 20% means you have to multiply by 1 − 0.2 = 0.8
⇒ 30 × 0.8 = £24

## Percentage Change

It is common to give a <u>change in value</u> as a <u>percentage</u>.
This is the formula for doing so — <u>LEARN IT, AND USE IT</u>:

$$\text{PERCENTAGE 'CHANGE'} = \frac{\text{'CHANGE'}}{\text{ORIGINAL}} \times 100$$

By 'change', we could mean all sorts of things such as: 'Profit', 'loss', 'appreciation',
'depreciation', 'increase', 'decrease', 'error', 'discount', etc. For example,

percentage 'loss' = $\frac{\text{'loss'}}{\text{original}}$ × 100   Note the great importance of using the
<u>ORIGINAL VALUE</u> in this formula.

### Example — Depreciation

David bought a new car last year for £11 995. By the end of the year,
the car was worth £7400.

Find the <u>percentage depreciation</u> in the value of the car over the first year.

<u>ANSWER</u>: "Depreciation" means a <u>decrease in value</u>,
so this is just a <u>percentage decrease</u> question.

% depreciation = $\frac{\text{depreciation}}{\text{original}}$ × 100

= $\frac{11\,995 - 7400}{11\,995}$ × 100 = <u>38.3%</u>

## Fact — 70% of people understand percentages, the other 40% don't...

Learn the details for the <u>different types of question</u> and <u>percentage change</u>, then <u>turn over</u> and <u>write it all down</u>.
1) Find £2.25 as a percentage of £18.
2) A car depreciates by 30% from £20 500. What is it worth now?
3) Find the percentage error in rounding 3.452 to 3.5. Give your answer to 2 D.P.

# Compound Interest and Depreciation

Compound growth is dead useful for working out how much interest you'll get in your savings account. Compound decay is kind of the opposite of that — and particularly useful for various science calculations. This can also be called 'Exponential' Growth or Decay (because the 'power number' is called the 'exponent').

## The Formula

This topic is simple if you **LEARN THIS FORMULA**. If you don't, it's pretty well impossible:

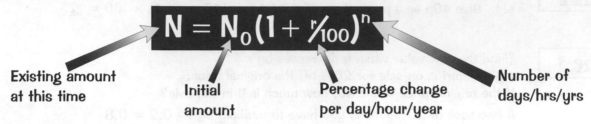

$$N = N_0\left(1 + \frac{r}{100}\right)^n$$

Existing amount at this time

Initial amount

Percentage change per day/hour/year

Number of days/hrs/yrs

## Percentage Increase and Decrease

The $(1 + r/100)$ bit might look a bit confusing in the formula but in practice it's really easy:

E.g 5% increase will be 1.05        5% decrease will be 0.95    $(= 1 - 0.05)$
        26% increase will be 1.26        26% decrease will be 0.74    $(= 1 - 0.26)$

## 3 Examples to show you how EASY it is:

1) "A man invests £1000 in a savings account which pays 8% per annum. How much will there be after 6 years?"

   **ANSWER:** Usual formula: Amount $= 1000(1.08)^6 = $ **£1586.87**

   Initial amount    8% increase    6 years

2) "A bicycle depreciates at a rate of 12% each year. If the bicycle cost £800 new, how much will it be worth after 7 years?"

   **ANSWER:** Same old formula:
   Value = Initial value$(1 - 12/100)^n$
   Value $= 800(1 - 0.12)^7 = 800 \times (0.88)^7 = $ **£326.94**

3) "In a sample of bacteria, there are initially 500 cells and they increase in number by 15% each day. Find the formula relating the number of cells, n and the number of days, d."

   **ANSWER:** Well stone me, it's the same old easy-peasy compound growth formula _again_:
   $n = n_0(1 + 0.15)^d$ or finished off: $\underline{n = 500 \times (1.15)^d}$

 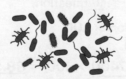 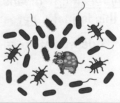

## Oh man, that last joke has still got me increases...

Bleurgh. What a horrible looking formula. 'Fraid you've still got to learn it though. And those three examples. Your reward though, is getting to do these questions. If you're struggling with them, go over the page again.

1) A colony of stick insects increases by 4% per week. Initially there are 30. How many will there be after 12 weeks?

2) The speed of a tennis ball rolled along a smooth floor falls by 16% every second. If the initial speed was 5 m/s find the speed after 20 seconds. How long will it take to stop?

# Ratios

The whole grisly subject of <u>RATIOS</u> gets a whole lot easier when you do this:

## Turn RATIOS into FRACTIONS

### What the fraction form of the ratio actually means

1) Suppose in a class there's <u>girls and boys</u> in the ratio 3 : 4.
   This means there's $\frac{3}{4}$ as many girls as boys.

2) So if there were 20 boys, there would be $\frac{3}{4} \times 20 = 15$ girls.
   You've got to be careful though — it <u>doesn't mean</u> $\frac{3}{4}$ of the <u>people</u> in the class are girls.
   In fact, <u>three sevenths</u> of the class are girls.

### Reducing Ratios to their simplest form

You reduce ratios just like you'd reduce fractions to their simplest form.

For the ratio 15:18, both numbers have a <u>factor</u> of 3, so <u>divide them by 3</u> — that
gives 5:6. We can't reduce this any further. So the simplest form of 15:18 is <u>5 : 6</u>.

#### Treat them just like fractions — use your calculator if you can

Now this is really sneaky. If you stick in a fraction using the $a\frac{b}{c}$ button,
your calculator automatically cancels it down when you press $=$.

So for the ratio 8:12, just press 8 $a\frac{b}{c}$ 12 $=$, and you'll get the reduced fraction $\frac{2}{3}$.
Now you just change it back to ratio form ie. <u>2 : 3</u>. Ace.

### The More Awkward Cases:

#### 1) The $a\frac{b}{c}$ button will only accept whole numbers

So if the ratio is something like '2.4 : 3.6' or '1¼ : 3½' then you must...

MULTIPLY BOTH SIDES by the SAME NUMBER until they are both WHOLE NUMBERS

E.g. for '1¼ : 3½', multiplying both sides by 4 gives '<u>5 : 14</u>' (Try $a\frac{b}{c}$, but it won't cancel further.)

#### 2) If the ratio is MIXED UNITS

CONVERT BOTH SIDES into the SMALLER UNITS using the relevant CONVERSION FACTOR (see P.16-17)

E.g. '24mm : 7.2cm' (× 7.2cm by 10) ⇒ 24mm : 72mm = <u>1 : 3</u> (using $a\frac{b}{c}$)

#### 3) To reduce a ratio to the form  1 : n or n : 1 (n can be any number)

Simply DIVIDE BOTH SIDES BY THE SMALLEST SIDE.

This form is often the <u>most useful</u>,
since it shows the ratio very clearly.

E.g. take "<u>3 : 56</u>" — dividing both sides by 3 gives: <u>1 : 18.7</u> (56÷3) (i.e. 1 : n)

# Ratios

There's just so much <u>great stuff</u> to say about ratios. I couldn't possibly fit it onto only one page...

## Using The Formula Triangle in Ratio Questions

**EXAMPLE:** "Mortar is made from sand and cement in the ratio 7:2. If 9 buckets of sand are used, how much cement is needed?"

This is a fairly common type of Exam question and it's pretty tricky for most people — but once you start using the formula triangle method, it's a bit of a breeze...

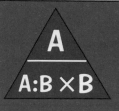

This is the basic <u>FORMULA TRIANGLE</u> for <u>RATIOS</u>, <u>but NOTE</u>:

1) <u>THE RATIO MUST BE THE RIGHT WAY ROUND</u>, with the <u>FIRST NUMBER IN THE RATIO</u> relating to <u>the item ON TOP</u> in the triangle.

2) <u>You'll always need to CONVERT THE RATIO</u> into its <u>EQUIVALENT FRACTION</u> or Decimal to work out the answer.

1) Here's the formula triangle for the mortar question...

2) The trick is to replace the ratio 7:2 by its <u>EQUIVALENT FRACTION</u> — 7/2, or 3.5 as a decimal (7÷2).

3) So, <u>covering up cement in the triangle</u>, gives us 'cement = sand / (7:2)' i.e. '9 / 3.5' = 9 ÷ 3.5 = 2.57 or about <u>2½ buckets of cement</u>.

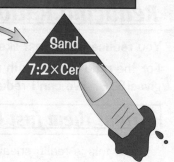

## Proportional Division

In a <u>proportional division</u> question a <u>TOTAL AMOUNT</u> is to be <u>split in a certain ratio</u>.

**EXAMPLE:** "£9100 is to be split in the ratio 2:4:7. Find the 3 amounts."

The key word here is <u>PARTS</u> — concentrate on 'parts' and it all becomes quite painless:

1) <u>ADD UP THE PARTS</u>:
The ratio 2:4:7 means there will be a total of 13 <u>parts</u>   i.e. 2+4+7 = <u>13 PARTS</u>

2) <u>FIND THE AMOUNT FOR ONE "PART"</u>
Just divide the <u>total amount</u> by the number of <u>parts</u>: £9100 ÷ 13 = <u>£700</u> (= 1 PART)

3) <u>HENCE FIND THE THREE AMOUNTS</u>:
2 parts = 2×700 = <u>£1400</u>,   4 parts = 4×700 = <u>£2800</u>,   7 parts = <u>£4900</u>

## Ratio Nelson — didn't he proportionally divide the French at Trafalgar...

Oh I do make myself chuckle. Learn the <u>rules for simplifying</u>, the <u>formula triangle for ratios</u>, and the <u>3 steps for proportional division</u>. Now turn over and <u>write down</u> what you've learned. Then try these:

1) Simplify:   a) 25:35   b) 3.4 : 5.1   c) 2¼ : 3¾
2) Porridge and ice-cream are mixed in the ratio 7:4.
   How much porridge should go with 10 bowls of ice-cream?
3) Divide £8400 in the ratio 5:3:4

# Rounding and Estimating

## Estimating

This is **VERY EASY**, so long as you don't <u>over-complicate it</u>.

> 1) **ROUND EVERYTHING OFF** to nice easy **CONVENIENT NUMBERS**.
> 2) Then **WORK OUT THE ANSWER** using these nice easy numbers — that's it!

<u>EXAMPLE:</u> Estimate the value of $\dfrac{127.8 + 41.9}{56.5 \times 3.2}$ showing all your working.

<u>ANSWER:</u> $\dfrac{127.8 + 41.9}{56.5 \times 3.2} \approx \dfrac{130 + 40}{60 \times 3} = \dfrac{170}{180} \approx 1$

*In the Exam you'll need to <u>show all the steps</u>, to prove you didn't just use a calculator.*

## Areas and Volumes

> 1) Draw or imagine a **RECTANGLE OR CUBOID** of similar size to the object.
> 2) **ROUND OFF** all lengths to the **NEAREST WHOLE**, and work it out — easy.

<u>EXAMPLE:</u> "Estimate the area of this shape:"

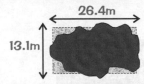

26.4m

13.1m

Area ≈ rectangle
26 m × 13 m = <u>338 m²</u>
(or without a calculator: 30 × 10 = 300 m²)

## Rounding — The Basic Method Has Three Steps

> 1) <u>Identify</u> the position of the **LAST DIGIT**.

> 2) Then look at the next digit to the **RIGHT** — called the **DECIDER**.

> 3) If the DECIDER is <u>5 or more</u>, then ROUND-UP the LAST DIGIT.
> If the DECIDER is <u>4 or less</u>, then leave the LAST DIGIT as it is.

There are <u>two different ways</u> of specifying <u>where</u> a number should be <u>rounded off</u>: 'Decimal Places' and 'Significant Figures'. Whichever way is used, the basic method is always the same.

> **EXAMPLE:** "What is 7.45839 to 2 Decimal Places?"
>
> $$7.4\,\fbox{5}\,\fbox{8}\,839 \qquad = \underline{7.46}$$
>
> **LAST DIGIT** to be written (2nd decimal place because we're rounding to 2 d.p.)    **DECIDER**    The **LAST DIGIT** rounds **UP** because the **DECIDER** is <u>5 or more</u>.

## It's official — this is the most exciting page of revision ever...

OK, so I might have exaggerated a little. Still, you've got to stay awake long enough to learn the <u>rules for estimating</u> and the <u>basic rounding method</u>. <u>Turn over</u> and <u>write down what you've learned</u>. Then have a crack at these:

1) Estimate the area of Great Britain in square miles, and the volume of a tin of beans in cm³.
2) Round 3.5743 to 2 decimal places.    3) Express 12.9096 to 2 decimal places.

*Unit 1 — Statistics and Probability*

# Rounding and Estimating

Obviously all numbers are significant, but when it comes to <u>rounding</u>, some are more significant than others...

## Decimal Places (D.P.)

This is pretty easy:

1) To round off to, say, <u>4 decimal places</u>, the <u>LAST DIGIT</u> will be the <u>4th one after the decimal point</u>.

2) There must be <u>no more digits</u> after the last digit (not even zeros).

> **EXAMPLE:**  Original number: <u>45.319461</u>
>
> Rounded to 5 decimal places (5 d.p.)   45.31946   (DECIDER was 1, so <u>don't</u> round up)
>
> Rounded to 4 decimal places (4 d.p.)   45.3195   (DECIDER was 6, so <u>do</u> round up)
>
> Rounded to 3 decimal places (3 d.p.)   45.319   (DECIDER was 4, so <u>don't</u> round up)

## Significant Figures (S.F.)

The method for significant figures is <u>identical</u> to that for decimal places except that finding the <u>position</u> of the <u>LAST DIGIT</u> is more difficult — <u>it wouldn't be so bad, but for the ZEROS</u>...

**1)** The <u>1st significant figure</u> of any number is simply THE FIRST DIGIT WHICH ISN'T A ZERO.

**2)** The <u>2nd, 3rd, 4th, etc. significant figures</u> follow on immediately after the 1st, REGARDLESS OF BEING ZEROS OR NOT ZEROS.

E.g          **0.002309**                    **2.03070**

<u>SIG FIGS</u>:      1st 2nd 3rd 4th          1st 2nd 3rd 4th

(If we're rounding to say, 3 s.f., then the LAST DIGIT is simply the 3rd sig. fig.)

*I asked Stacey for her significant figures.*
*Data?*
*Nah, we're just friends.*

**3)** After <u>Rounding Off</u> the LAST DIGIT, <u>end ZEROS</u> must be filled in <u>up to, BUT NOT BEYOND, the decimal point</u>.

No <u>extra zeros</u> must ever be put in <u>after</u> the decimal point.

| Examples | to 4 s.f. | to 3 s.f. | to 2 s.f. | to 1 s.f. |
|----------|-----------|-----------|-----------|-----------|
| 1) 54.7651 | 54.77 | 54.8 | 55 | 50 |
| 2) 17.0067 | 17.01 | 17.0 | 17 | 20 |
| 3) 0.0045902 | 0.004590 | 0.00459 | 0.0046 | 0.005 |
| 4) 30895.4 | 30900 | 30900 | 31000 | 30000 |

<u>WARNING</u> — be careful of rounding numbers in the <u>middle of a calculation</u>, as you could get <u>rounding errors</u>.  Much better to round your answer at the <u>end</u>.

## Julius Caesar, Henry VIII, Winston Churchill, 3 — all significant figures...

<u>Learn the whole of this page</u>, then turn over and <u>write down everything you've learned</u>.  And for pudding...

1) Round these to 2 d.p. :   a) 3.408   b) 1.051   c) 0.068   d) 3.596

2) Round these to 3 s.f. :   a) 567.78   b) 23445   c) 0.04563   d) 0.90876

# Probability

This is nobody's favourite subject for sure, I've never really spoken to anyone who's said they do like it (not for long anyway). Although it does seem a bit of a 'Black Art' to most people, it's not as bad as you might think, but <u>YOU MUST LEARN THE BASIC FACTS</u>.

## All Probabilities are between 0 and 1

A probability of <u>ZERO</u> means it will <u>NEVER HAPPEN</u>.
A probability of <u>ONE</u> means it <u>DEFINITELY WILL</u>.

<u>You can't have a probability bigger than 1</u>.

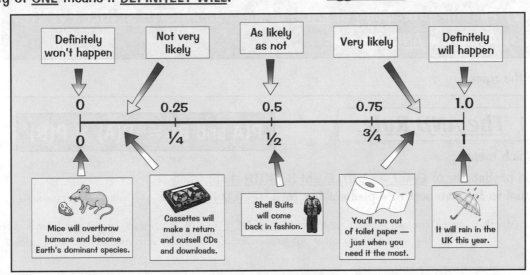

You should be able to put the probability of any event happening on this scale from 0 to 1.

## Three Important Details

1) Probabilities should be given as either
   a <u>FRACTION (¼)</u>, or a <u>DECIMAL (0.25)</u> or a <u>PERCENTAGE (25%)</u>
2) The notation 'P(X) = ½' should be read as:
   '<u>THE PROBABILITY OF EVENT X HAPPENING IS ½</u>'
3) Probabilities <u>ALWAYS ADD UP TO 1</u>. This is essential for finding the
   probability of the other outcome. E.g. If P(pass) = ¼, then P(fail) = ¾

## Listing All Outcomes: 2 Coins, Dice, Spinners

A simple question you might get is to list all the possible results from
tossing two coins or two spinners or a dice and a spinner, etc.
Whatever it is, it'll be very similar to these, so <u>LEARN THEM</u>:

The <u>possible outcomes</u> from <u>TOSSING TWO COINS</u> are:

| Head | Head | H | H |
|------|------|---|---|
| Head | Tail | H | T |
| Tail | Head | T | H |
| Tail | Tail | T | T |

List the possible outcomes <u>METHODICALLY</u>
to make sure you get them <u>ALL</u>.

1) A <u>SAMPLE SPACE DIAGRAM</u> is basically
   a posh name for a <u>table</u>. If you use one,
   you're less likely to <u>miss out</u> any outcomes.

2) This table shows all the outcomes
   from <u>TWO SPINNERS</u>, one with
   3 colours and the other with
   <u>numbers from 1 to 3</u>:

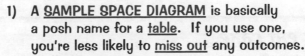

|   | Red | Blue | Green |
|---|-----|------|-------|
| 1 | 1R  | 1B   | 1G    |
| 2 | 2R  | 2B   | 2G    |
| 3 | 3R  | 3B   | 3G    |

# Probability

This is where most people start getting into trouble, and d'you know why?
I'll tell you — it's because they don't know the <u>three simple steps</u> and the <u>two rules</u> to apply:

## Three Simple Steps

1) Always break down a complicated-looking probability question into <u>A SEQUENCE</u> of <u>SEPARATE SINGLE EVENTS</u>.
2) Find the probability of <u>EACH</u> of these <u>SEPARATE SINGLE EVENTS</u>.
3) Apply the <u>AND/OR</u> rule:

And now for the rules...

## 1) The AND Rule:

$$P(A \text{ and } B) = P(A) \times P(B)$$

Which means:

The probability of <u>Event A  AND  Event B  BOTH  happening</u> is
equal to the two separate probabilities <u>MULTIPLIED together</u>.

(strictly speaking, the two events have to be <u>INDEPENDENT</u>. All that means is that one event happening
does not in any way affect the other one happening. Contrast this with mutually exclusive below.)

## 2) The OR Rule:

$$P(A \text{ or } B) = P(A) + P(B)$$

Which means:

The probability of <u>EITHER Event A OR Event B happening</u> is
equal to the two separate probabilities <u>ADDED together</u>.

(Strictly speaking, the two events have to be <u>MUTUALLY EXCLUSIVE</u>
which means that if one event happens, the other one can't happen.)

The way to remember this is that it's the <u>wrong way round</u> — i.e. you'd want the AND to go
with the + but it doesn't: It's '<u>AND with ×</u>' and '<u>OR with +</u>'.

### Example

"Find the probability of picking two kings from a pack of cards
(assuming you don't replace the first card picked)."

1) <u>SPLIT</u> this into <u>TWO SEPARATE EVENTS</u> — i.e. picking the <u>first king</u> and then <u>picking the second king</u>.

2) <u>Find the SEPARATE probabilities</u> of these two <u>separate events</u>:
$P(\text{1st king}) = \frac{4}{52}$     $P(\text{2nd king}) = \frac{3}{51}$     (— note the change from 52 to 51)

3) <u>Apply the AND/OR rule</u>:    <u>BOTH</u> events must happen, so it's the <u>AND</u> rule:
so <u>multiply</u> the two separate probabilities: $\frac{4}{52} \times \frac{3}{51} = \frac{1}{221}$

## Revise — and/or eat cake...

Wowsers, lots of important stuff on those two pages. Learn the <u>three simple steps</u> for <u>multiple events</u>, and the
<u>AND/OR rule</u> and you'll be fine and/or dandy in the exam. Ahem. Now have a go at these little jokers below...

1) Find the probability of picking from a pack of cards (without replacement):
   a) 2 queens plus the ace of spades.  b) A <u>pair</u> of Jacks, Queens or Kings

# Probability — Relative Frequency

This isn't the number of times your granny comes to visit. It's a way of working out <u>probabilities</u>. Since you asked, my granny visits twice a year. She says she'd like to visit more, but sleeping on the blow-up bed plays <u>havoc</u> with her bad back.

## Fair or Biased?

The probability of rolling a three on a dice is $\frac{1}{6}$ — you know that each of the 6 numbers on a dice is <u>equally likely</u> to be rolled, and there's <u>only 1 three</u>.

BUT this only works if it's a <u>fair dice</u>. If the dice is a bit <u>wonky</u> (the technical term is '<u>biased</u>') then each number <u>won't</u> have an equal chance of being rolled. That's where <u>relative frequency</u> comes in — you can use it to work out probabilities when things might be wonky.

## Do the Experiment Again and Again and Again and Again

You need to do an experiment <u>over and over again</u> and then do a quick calculation. (Remember, an experiment could just mean rolling a dice.) Usually the results of these experiments will be written in a <u>table</u>.

### The Formula for Relative Frequency

$$\text{Probability of something happening} = \frac{\text{Number of times it has happened}}{\text{Number of times you tried}}$$

You can work out the relative frequency as a <u>fraction</u> but usually <u>decimals</u> are best for comparing relative frequencies.

The important thing to remember is:

The more times you <u>DO THE EXPERIMENT</u>, the <u>MORE ACCURATE</u> the probability will be.

### Example

So, back to the wonky dice. <u>What is the probability of rolling a three</u>?

| Number of Times the dice was rolled | 10 | 20 | 50 | 100 |
|---|---|---|---|---|
| Number of Threes rolled | 2 | 5 | 11 | 23 |
| Relative Frequency | $\frac{2}{10} = 0.2$ | $\frac{5}{20} = 0.25$ | $\frac{11}{50} = 0.22$ | $\frac{23}{100} = 0.23$ |

We've got <u>4 possible answers</u>, but the best is the one worked out using the <u>highest number of dice rolls</u>. This makes the probability of rolling a three on this dice <u>0.23</u>. And since for a fair, unbiased dice, the probability of rolling a three is $\frac{1}{6}$ (about 0.17), then our dice is probably <u>biased</u>.

## Dice rolls — a crunchy packed lunch alternative...

Blast those wonky dice. That's what started all this. Still it's all bound to come up on the exam — so learn the formula for calculating <u>relative frequency</u>. Then it's time to test yourself with a question. Oh, like the one here...

1) Bill picks a card at random out of a pack and then replaces it. He does this 100 times, and picks a total of 13 aces. Do you think the pack is biased? Why?

# Probability — Tree Diagrams

Tree diagrams are all pretty much the same, so it's a pretty darned good idea to learn these basic details (which apply to __ALL__ tree diagrams) — ready for the one that's bound to be in the Exam.

## General Tree Diagram

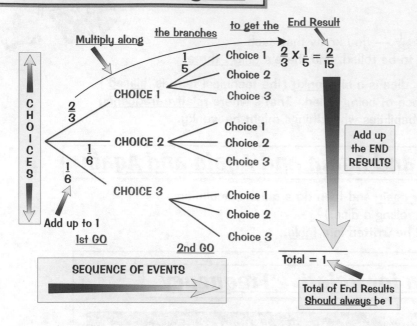

1) Always __MULTIPLY ALONG__ the branches (as shown) to get the __END RESULTS__.

2) On any set of branches which all __meet at a point__, the numbers must always __ADD UP TO 1__.

3) __Check__ that your diagram is correct by making sure the end results __ADD UP TO ONE__.

4) To answer any question, simply __ADD UP__ the relevant __END RESULTS__ (see below).

## A Likely Tree Diagram Question

__EXAMPLE:__ "A box contains 5 red disks and 3 green disks. Two disks are taken at random __without replacement__. Draw a tree diagram and hence find the probability that both disks are the same colour."

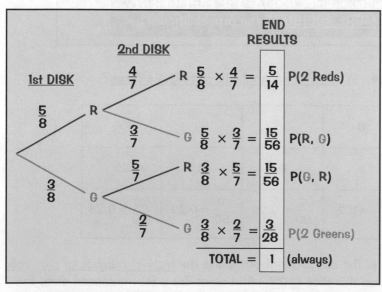

Once the tree diagram is drawn all you then need to do to answer the question is simply select the relevant __END RESULTS__ and then __ADD THEM TOGETHER:__

2 REDS     (5/14)
2 GREENS    (3/28)

$$\frac{5}{14} + \frac{3}{28} = \frac{13}{28}$$

If you can, use a calculator for this.

## General Tree Diagram reporting for duty sir...

How convenient — answers growing on trees. You still need to learn the __general tree diagram__ and the __4 points__ that go with it though — just in case there's a disappointing harvest. I'll leave you to have a go at these...

1) OK, let's see what you've learnt shall we: turn over and write down everything you know about tree diagrams.
2) A bag contains 6 red tarantulas and 4 black tarantulas. If two girls each pluck out a tarantula at random, draw a tree diagram to find the probability that they get different coloured ones.

# Probability — Tree Diagrams

## Four Extra Details for the Tree Diagram method:

### 1) Always break up the question into a SEQUENCE of Separate events.

E.g. '3 coins are tossed together' — just split it into 3 separate events.
You need this sequence of events to be able to draw any sort of tree diagram.

### 2) Don't feel you have to draw complete tree diagrams.

Learn to adapt them to what is required. E.g. 'What is the chance of
throwing a dice 3 times and getting 2 sixes followed by an even number?'

This diagram is all you need to get the answer: $\frac{1}{6} \times \frac{1}{6} \times \frac{1}{2} = \frac{1}{72}$

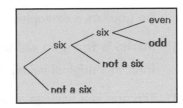

### 3) Watch out for conditional probabilities...

...where the fraction on each branch depends on what happened <u>on the previous branch</u>, e.g. bags of sweets, packs of cards etc, where the <u>bottom</u> number of the fractions <u>also</u> changes as items are removed. E.g. $\frac{11}{25}$ then $\frac{10}{24}$ etc.

My parents wanted at least one girl.

### 4) With 'AT LEAST' questions, it's always (1 − Prob of 'the other outcome'):

For example, 'Find the probability of having AT LEAST one girl in 4 children.'
There are in fact <u>15 different ways</u> of having 'AT LEAST one girl in 4 children'
which would take a long time to work out, even with a tree diagram.

The clever trick you should know is this:
The prob of 'AT LEAST something or other' is just (1 − prob of 'the other outcome')
which in this case is (1 − prob of 'all 4 boys') = $(1 - \frac{1}{16}) = \frac{15}{16}$.

### Example

"Herbert and his two chums, along with five of Herbert's doting aunties, have to squeeze onto the back seat of his father's Bentley, en route to Royal Ascot. Given that Herbert does not sit at either end, and that the seating order is otherwise random, find the probability of Herbert having his best chums either side of him."

The untrained probabilist wouldn't think of using a tree diagram here,
but see how easy it is when you do. <u>This is the tree diagram you'd draw</u>:

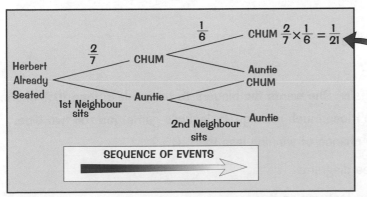

So the <u>answer</u> is $\frac{1}{21}$.
Of course you'd have to do a bit of thinking to decide to place Herbert first and then have the two events as each of his 'neighbours' are placed beside him.

## Things that grow on trees summary: answers = yes, money = no...

Learn the whole of this page, cover it up and write down the <u>key points</u> and the <u>example</u> too. Simples.

1) As it turned out, the Bentley could only seat 6 people across so the last two in had to sit on other people's laps. Find the probability that Herbert had his best chums either side and no doting Auntie on his lap (assuming Herbert wasn't one of the last 2).

# Revision Summary for Unit 1 — Part 1

I know these questions seem difficult, but they are the very best revision you can do.
The whole point of revision, remember, is to find out what you don't know and then learn it until you do.
These searching questions test how much you know better than anything else ever can.
They follow the sequence of pages in the Unit, so you can easily look up anything you don't know.

## KEEP LEARNING THESE BASIC FACTS UNTIL YOU KNOW THEM

1) Do your own examples to illustrate each of the three types of percentage question.

2)* Martin is trying to sell his car. He paid £5300 for it two years ago and is advised to sell it for 30% less than this original value. What price should he sell the car for?

3)* Tim opens a savings account that pays 7% compound interest per annum.
He puts £100 into the account. How much will he have after 5 years?

4)* Sarah is in charge of ordering new stock for a clothes shop. The shop usually sells red scarves and blue scarves in the ratio 5:8. Sarah orders 150 red scarves. How many blue scarves should she order?

5) What are the three steps of the method of proportional division?

6)* Jill, Heather and Susie spent Saturday helping out in their mum's cafe. Jill worked for 3 hours, Heather worked the next 2.5 hours and Susie worked for the final 1.5 hours of the day. They were given £42 to split between them for the work they'd done. How much should each of them receive?

7)* Jenny and two of her friends went out for dinner. The bill came to £51.98 and they decided to split it equally. How much, to two decimal places, should each of them pay?

8)* Chris plans to wallpaper a wall that is 4.17 m high and 11.85 m wide.
The wallpaper he wants to use is 60 cm wide and comes in 5 m-long rolls.
How many rolls of wallpaper should he buy?

9) What is the numerical probability of an event which:
   a) is certain?
   b) is impossible?
   c) has an even chance?

10) What are the AND and OR rules of probability?

11) What's the formula for relative frequency?

12)* Jackie is preparing a game for the school fair. She wants the players to have a less than 10% chance of winning to make sure the school doesn't lose much money. In Jackie's game you roll two dice. If you roll two sixes you win £20. Is the chance of winning less than 10%?

13) Write down four important facts about tree diagrams.

14) Draw a general tree diagram and put all the features on it.

# Data Collection

Data is what <u>statistics</u> is all about.  You've got to <u>collect</u> it, <u>process</u> it and then <u>interpret</u> it.

## Start With a Research Question...

1) A <u>research question</u> is just a general question about a topic you want to know about.

2) It's usually quite a <u>broad question</u> e.g. what do people have for lunch?  How do people get to work?  So you should <u>break it down</u> into more manageable chunks by coming up with some <u>sub-questions</u>:

> **EXAMPLE**  A tourist board wants to investigate the number of people that go to the beach.  Suggest <u>three</u> possible sub-questions they could ask.
>
> Some possible <u>sub-questions</u> might be:
> * Do more people go to the beach when the weather is warm?
> * Is the beach more popular on a Sunday?
> * Do more people go to the beach when the schools are on holiday?

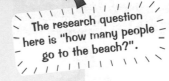
The research question here is "how many people go to the beach?".

Once you have your question you can start to <u>collect data</u> to answer it...

## Choose an Appropriate Source of Data

1) The first thing to do is <u>identify exactly</u> what data you <u>need</u>.

2) Then you need to weigh up the <u>pros</u> and <u>cons</u> of using either <u>primary</u> or <u>secondary</u> data:

| **<u>PRIMARY</u> data is data <u>you've</u> collected.** | **<u>SECONDARY</u> data is collected by <u>someone else</u>.** |
|---|---|
| 1) There are the <u>two</u> main ways you can gather <u>primary data</u>:<br><br>A <u>SURVEY</u>, e.g. a <u>questionnaire</u> (p.22).<br>An <u>EXPERIMENT</u> — when you <u>measure</u> how one thing <u>changes</u> when you change something else.<br><br>2) Primary data is often <u>RAW DATA</u> — data that hasn't been processed. | 1) There are lots of ways you can get hold of secondary data, e.g. from <u>newspapers</u>, <u>magazines</u>, the <u>internet</u>, <u>databases</u> and <u>historical records</u>.<br><br>2) You can also get data from the <u>Office for National Statistics</u>, which gathers data about the <u>economy</u>, <u>social trends</u> and the <u>environment</u>.<br><br>3) Secondary data has normally been <u>PROCESSED</u> before you get it, e.g. it might be presented as a percentage, graph or table. |

3) Once you've chosen a source of data, you need to weigh up the <u>pros</u> and <u>cons</u> of <u>methods</u> of data collection (e.g. questionnaire, telephone interview, observation, experiment etc.)

> **EXAMPLE**  Wartshire Council wants to know how far people from different districts travel to work.
> a) Say <u>what pieces</u> of data the council needs to collect.
> b) Do you think <u>primary</u> or <u>secondary</u> data would be more <u>appropriate</u>.
> c) Suggest a <u>method</u> the council could use to collect the data it needs.
>
> a) The council would need to collect data on <u>how far</u> people travel to work and <u>where</u> they live.
> b) <u>Primary data</u> — it's unlikely that there would be a secondary source they could use.
> c) A <u>questionnaire</u> seems like a sensible way to collect this information.

## Red or brown — choose an appropriate sauce...

Make sure you're clear on research questions, sub-questions and types of data.  Then have a pop at this...
1) A student has a question: "Do more people have school dinners on a Thursday than any other day?"
   a) What data is needed to answer this question?
   b) Suggest a suitable method of data collection that the student could use.

# Types of Data

Your data might be <u>quantitative</u> or <u>qualitative</u>...

## Data can be Quantitative or Qualitative

**QUANTITATIVE DATA** measures <u>quantities</u>.

1) <u>Quantitative data</u> is anything that you can measure with a <u>number</u>.
2) For example, <u>heights</u> of people, the <u>time taken</u> to complete a task or the <u>mass</u> of things.
3) Quantitative data tends to be <u>easier to analyse</u> than qualitative data.

**QUALITATIVE DATA** is <u>descriptive</u>.

1) <u>Qualitative data</u> is data that uses <u>words</u> to <u>describe it</u> — it doesn't use any numbers.
2) For example, <u>gender</u>, eye <u>colour</u> or <u>how nice</u> a curry is.
3) This sort of data is usually <u>harder to analyse</u> than quantitative data.

## Quantitative Data is Either Discrete or Continuous

**DISCRETE DATA** is data that can be recorded <u>exactly</u>.

1) If your data is something that's <u>countable</u> in whole numbers or can only take certain <u>individual values</u>, it's called <u>discrete data</u>.
2) Things like the <u>number of points</u> scored in a game, the <u>number of people</u> going into a shop on a Saturday and the <u>number of pages</u> in this revision guide are all examples of discrete data.

**CONTINUOUS DATA** is data that can take <u>any value</u> in an interval.

1) If your data is something that could <u>always</u> be <u>more accurately measured</u>, it's continuous data.
2) The <u>height</u> of <u>this page</u> is an example of continuous data. The height is 297 mm to the nearest mm, but you'd get a <u>more accurate</u> height if you measured to the nearest 0.1 mm or 0.01 mm or 0.001 mm or 0.0001 mm, etc... The actual height could take <u>any value</u> in the interval 296.5 mm to 297.5 mm.
3) Other things like the <u>weight</u> of a pumpkin, the <u>age</u> of a chicken and the <u>length</u> of a carrot are continuous data.

## You can Split your Data into Classes

1) If you're collecting <u>lots of data</u>, or your data's <u>spread out</u> over a large range, you can make it more manageable by <u>grouping it</u> into different <u>classes</u>.

2) When you do this, it's important that you <u>define the classes well</u> so <u>none of them overlap</u> — this means that each bit of data can <u>only</u> be put into <u>one class</u>.

| Age in completed years | 0 – 19 | 20 – 39 | 40 – 59 | 60 – 79 | 80 – 99 |
|---|---|---|---|---|---|
| Number of people | 6 | 13 | 14 | 8 | 9 |

3) The <u>problem</u> with grouping data is that you <u>lose</u> some of the <u>accuracy</u> of it because you don't know what the <u>exact data values</u> are any more.

## Sorry, I can't date 'er — she's just not my type...

Nothing too complicated here, just a few more definitions to learn. Once you've got 'em, try this question:
1) Say whether this data is qualitative, discrete or continuous:
   a) The number of spectators at a rugby match.
   b) The colours of pebbles on a beach.
   c) The nationalities of people visiting a museum on a certain day.
   d) The lengths of fish in Windermere.

# Sampling

My top tip for stats revision: keep yourself awake with a big vat of <u>coffee</u>, a regular blare of <u>loud music</u> and an occasional dance of the <u>hokey cokey</u>. If you don't fancy that, carry on with this page...

## Population — The Group You Want to Find Out About

1) For any statistical project, you need to find out information about a group of people or things. This group is called the <u>POPULATION</u>. Examples of populations are:
   - All the pupils in a school.
   - All people who have access to the internet.
   - All the boxes of cereal produced by a factory.
   - All the newts living in a pond.

2) You collect information about a population by doing a <u>SURVEY</u> — it can be used to collect data about the <u>whole population</u> or from a <u>SAMPLE</u> (<u>part of the population</u>).

## Sampling — Cheaper and Easier than Asking Everyone

1) Choosing <u>only a few</u> members of a population is called <u>SAMPLING</u> — surveying a sample is a relatively <u>easy</u> way of finding out about a population.

2) You can use the data you collect to make <u>estimates</u> and <u>draw conclusions</u> about the <u>whole population</u>.

3) E.g. Pete needs to find out about the heights of trees in a <u>forest</u> for his biology project. Measuring every tree would take ages so he uses a <u>sample of 500 trees</u> to represent the whole population.

4) There are <u>pros</u> and <u>cons</u> of using <u>sample data</u>:

**PROS** It's a lot <u>quicker</u>, <u>cheaper</u> and often <u>more practical</u> than doing a survey of the entire population.

**CONS** You <u>don't</u> have information about <u>every member</u> of the population so it can be less accurate.

It's really important that your sample is <u>REPRESENTATIVE</u> — it has to be <u>unbiased</u> and <u>big enough</u> (see p.21).

## Make Sure Your Population is Well Defined

1) Before you can choose a sample, you need to know <u>EXACTLY WHAT YOUR POPULATION IS</u>.

2) You should make a <u>list</u> or <u>map</u> of <u>all the members</u> of the population — this is called a <u>SAMPLE FRAME</u>.

3) It's easiest to do this with a <u>small well-defined population</u> because:
   - if it's <u>small</u> it's easier to <u>list everything</u>.
   - if it's <u>well defined</u> you know exactly what needs to be included.

**EXAMPLE** A student is trying to find out the <u>average Key Stage 2 SATs score</u> for <u>Maths</u> in <u>England</u> in 2009. State the <u>population</u> and <u>sample frame</u> in this example.

The <u>population</u> would be all students in England who took the Key Stage 2 Maths SAT in 2009.

The <u>sample frame</u> would be a <u>list</u> of all students who took the Key Stage 2 Maths SAT in 2009.

## I thought a sampling was a baby tree diagram...

It's all pretty obvious if you think about it. Learn the stuff on this page and then have a go at these fab questions:
1) What's the sample frame if a doctor's surgery wants to know the ages of people registered at the surgery?
2) Explain whether a survey on the music listening preferences of a school that uses a Year 7 class as a sample is likely to be representative.

# Sampling Methods

Sampling is a good thing — but you can't just go round choosing the things you like the look of. You have to choose members of your sample AT RANDOM.

## Choosing Things at Random

Something is chosen at random when every item in a group has an equal chance of being chosen.

> For example, if you had a bag with 3 different coloured snooker balls in it and picked one out without looking, it would be random because all the balls have an equal chance of being picked.

## Simple Random Sampling — Choosing a Random Sample

1) In a simple random sample, you randomly select your sample from the sample frame (see p.19).

2) It's easiest to do this type of sampling with a small, well defined population.

3) To select the sample you need to use random numbers. Here's how you do it:

> ① Assign a number to every member in the sample frame.
> ② Use a computer, calculator or random number table to create a list of random numbers.
> ③ Finally, match the numbers of the members in the sample frame to the numbers on the random list to create the sample.

Albert wasn't so keen on the random thought generator

4) Simple random sampling is sometimes too difficult to use so you need some other tricks up your sleeve...

## Stratified Sampling — Proportional Representation

1) Sometimes the population might be made up of groups or categories that contain members which are similar to each other in some way, e.g. age groups or gender.

2) In these cases you can use STRATIFIED SAMPLING. This makes sure the proportion of people in each group is the same in the sample as it is in the whole population — which means big groups get more representation and small groups get less.

3) Then you choose the right number from each group at random to make your sample.

---

**EXAMPLE**  The table on the right shows the distribution of students at Eastfield Secondary School by year group. Describe how you could use stratified sampling to choose a sample of 50 students from the 1000 students at the school.

| Year 9 | Year 10 | Year 11 |
|--------|---------|---------|
| 400 | 400 | 200 |

Find the proportion of students that are in each year group and multiply this by the total number you want in the sample.

$$\frac{\text{total in year}}{\text{total number of students}} \times \text{size of sample} = \text{number of students to be picked}$$

So... Year 9 = (400 / 1000) × 50 = 20

Year 10 = (400 / 1000) × 50 = 20

Year 11 = (200 / 1000) × 50 = 10

This should give a representative sample, with the right proportion of students from each year group.

---

## Random Stat. #387 — "sample" is used 15 times on this page...

Two sampling strategies to learn on this page — then try this fantastical question:

1) A company has 10 senior managers, 22 middle managers and 68 shop-floor workers. A representative committee of 10 employees is to be chosen using stratified random sampling. How many of each type of employee would need to be in the sample?

# Sampling Methods

All sampling methods can be affected by <u>bias</u>.
So, to make sure you can <u>spot a biased sample</u> a mile off, here's a page about them...

## Be Careful — Sample Data Must be Representative

1) When you sample a population it's <u>important</u> to make sure the sample <u>fairly represents</u> the <u>whole population</u>. This means any <u>conclusions</u> you draw from the data in the sample can be <u>applied</u> to the <u>whole population</u>.

2) A <u>BIASED study</u> is one that <u>doesn't fairly represent</u> the <u>whole population</u>.
   To avoid bias you need to:

   - Sample from the <u>CORRECT POPULATION</u>. This means only choosing things <u>from the sample frame</u> (see p.19) and making sure none of the sample frame is <u>excluded</u>.
   - Select your sample at <u>RANDOM</u> (see previous page).

3) A <u>bigger sample</u> is <u>better</u> because it's more likely to be <u>representative IF</u> you're sampling the <u>right population</u>. It'll provide <u>more reliable data</u> — but it might be <u>less practical</u> to <u>collect</u>.

## Spotting Problems With Sampling Methods

In practice, the most important thing you should be able to do is spot problems with sampling techniques, which means look for ways that the sample might <u>not be a true reflection of the population</u>.
One mildly amusing way to practise, is to think up examples of bad sampling techniques:

1) A survey of motorists carried out in London concluded that 85% of British people drive Black Cabs.

2) Two surveys carried out on the same street corner asked, "Do you believe in God?" One found 90% of people didn't and the other found 90% of people did. The reason for the discrepancy? — one was carried out at 11pm Saturday night and the other at 10.15am Sunday morning.

3) A telephone survey carried out in the evening asked, "What do you usually do after work or school?". It found that 80% of the population usually stay in and watch TV. A street survey conducted at the same time found that only 30% usually stay in and watch TV. Astonishing.

<u>Other cases are less obvious:</u>
In a telephone poll, 100 people were asked if they use the train regularly and 20% said yes. Does this mean 20% of the population regularly use the train?

<u>ANSWER</u>: <u>Probably not</u>. There are <u>several things wrong with this sampling technique</u>:
- <u>First and worst</u>: the sample is <u>far too small</u>. <u>At least 1000</u> would be more like it.
- What about people who don't have their own phone?
- What time of day was it done? When might regular train users be in or out?
- Which part or parts of the country were telephoned?
- If the results were to represent, say, the whole country, then <u>stratified sampling</u> would be essential.

## When getting a sample — size matters...

...so that it's more representative. Make sure you understand what the problems are with sampling methods and why sample data has to be representative. Then time for a question...

1) A survey was done to investigate the average age of cars on Britain's roads by standing on a motorway bridge and noting the registration of the first 200 cars. Give three reasons why this is a poor sampling technique and suggest a better approach.

# Questionnaires

Questionnaires are a good way of collecting data — they're <u>cheap</u> and <u>easy to distribute</u> over a wide area...

## Design your Questionnaire Carefully

Bear these <u>six points</u> in mind when you <u>design</u> a questionnaire:

**1** MAKE SURE YOUR QUESTIONS ARE RELEVANT

It's no good asking really <u>fascinating</u> questions if the answers aren't going to be useful.

**2** QUESTIONS SHOULD BE <u>CLEAR</u>, <u>BRIEF</u> AND <u>EASY TO UNDERSTAND</u>

Your best bet is to assume that the people answering them are really stupid.

**3** ALLOW FOR <u>ALL POSSIBLE ANSWERS</u> TO YOUR QUESTION

E.g. "What is your favourite subject: Maths, English or Science?" is difficult to answer <u>truthfully</u> if you like Art best — to help, you could add an "other" category.

**4** QUESTIONS SHOULDN'T BE <u>LEADING OR BIASED</u>

<u>Leading</u> or <u>biased questions</u> are ones that <u>suggest</u> what answer is wanted.
For example: "Do you agree that thrash metal is really good music?"
The problem with this question is that it could make the interviewee feel pressurised into saying 'yes'. A better question would be "What type of music do you prefer to listen to?"

**5** QUESTIONS SHOULD BE <u>UNAMBIGUOUS</u>

Here's an example: "Do you play computer games a lot?"
This question could be <u>interpreted differently</u> by different people. One person could answer <u>yes</u>, while another who plays the same amount could answer <u>no</u>. A <u>better question</u> would be "How many hours do you play computer games per week?" because it isn't open to different interpretations.

**6** PEOPLE MAY NOT ANSWER QUESTIONS <u>TRUTHFULLY</u>

This is often because they're <u>embarrassed</u> about the answer. For example "What is your age?" might be a <u>sensitive question</u> for some people. You can get round this by using groups so they don't have to answer with their exact age.

## Distributing and Collecting Questionnaires can Lead to Bias

There are several ways you could distribute your questionnaire, but they all have their own <u>disadvantages</u>.
- <u>Send it in the post</u> — this will reach a <u>big area</u>, but you <u>can't be sure</u> who will <u>receive</u> and <u>answer</u> it. E.g. as a prank, children sometimes fill in questionnaires intended for their parents.
- <u>Ask people to pick one up</u> — e.g. a customer satisfaction questionnaire in a restaurant. However, only people who've had <u>very good</u> or <u>very bad</u> service are likely to fill in the questionnaire.
- <u>Hand them out</u> — this ensures the target population gets the questionnaire but is very <u>time consuming</u>.

Some people <u>WON'T RESPOND</u> to your questionnaire. It could be for <u>many reasons</u> but it's often because people <u>can't be bothered</u>. Here are some things you can do to <u>improve the response</u>:
- Use really <u>clear questions</u> that are <u>simple</u> and <u>easy to answer</u>.
- <u>Follow up</u> people who don't respond, e.g. go and <u>collect</u> their questionnaires in person.
- Provide an <u>incentive</u> for them to answer, e.g. enter them into a prize draw.

## Who wants to collect a questionnaire...

... is the (not so exciting) quiz spin-off. Make sure you learn the whole page and then try this question...
1) Give one criticism of each of these questions:   a) Do you watch a lot of television?
   b) Do you agree that maths is the most important subject taught in schools?
   c) What is your favourite drink? Answer A, B or C.   A) Tea     B) Milk     C) Coffee

# Mean, Median, Mode and Range

If you don't manage to learn these 4 basic definitions then you'll be passing up
on some of the easiest marks in the whole Exam. It can't be that difficult can it?

1) **MODE** = **MOST** common

2) **MEDIAN** = **MIDDLE** value

3) **MEAN** = **TOTAL** of items ÷ **NUMBER** of items

4) **RANGE** = How far from the smallest to the biggest

**REMEMBER:**
Mode = most (emphasise the 'o'
in each when you say them)
Median = mid (emphasise the m*d
in each when you say them)
Mean is just the average, but it's
mean 'cos you have to work it out.

## The Golden Rule

Mean, median and mode should be easy marks but even people who've gone to the incredible extent
of learning them still manage to lose marks in the Exam because they don't do this one vital step:

### Always REARRANGE the data in ASCENDING ORDER

(and check you have the same number of entries!)

## Example

"Find the mean, median, mode and range of these numbers:"
2, 5, 3, 2, 6, -4, 0, 9, -3, 1, 6, 3, -2, 3        (14)

1) FIRST... rearrange them:   -4, -3, -2, 0, 1, 2, 2, 3, 3, 3, 5, 6, 6, 9 (14) ✓

2) MEAN = $\dfrac{\text{total of items}}{\text{number of items}}$ = $\dfrac{-4-3-2+0+1+2+2+3+3+3+5+6+6+9}{14}$

   = 31 ÷ 14 = **2.21**

3) MEDIAN = the middle value (only when they are arranged in order of size, that is!).

   When there are two middle numbers
   as in this case, then the median is
   **HALFWAY BETWEEN THE
   TWO MIDDLE NUMBERS**.

   -4, -3, -2, 0, 1, 2, 2, 3, 3, 3, 5, 6, 6, 9
   ← seven numbers this side  ↑  seven numbers this side →
   Median = **2.5**

4) MODE = most common value, which is simply **3**. (Or you can say, "The modal value is 3.")

5) RANGE = distance from lowest to highest value, i.e. from -4 up to 9 = **13**

## Choosing the Best Average

The mean, median and mode
all have their advantages and
disadvantages — **LEARN THEM**:

|        | Advantages | Disadvantages |
|--------|-----------|---------------|
| Mean   | Uses all the data<br>Usually most representative | Isn't always a data value<br>May be distorted by outliers |
| Median | Easy to find in ordered data<br>Not distorted by outliers | Isn't always a data value<br>Not always a good representation of the data |
| Mode   | Easy to find in tallied data<br>Always a data value | Doesn't always exist or sometimes more than one<br>Not always a good representation of the data |

## Strike a pose, there's nothing to it — mode...

Learn the four definitions and the golden rule... then turn this page over and write them down from memory.
Then apply all that you have learnt to this set of data: 1, 3, 14, -5, 6, -12, 18, 7, 23, 10, -5, -14, 0, 25, 8.

# Quartiles and the Interquartile Range

Now we're getting to the good stuff. And by good stuff, I mean <u>quartiles</u> and <u>interquartile</u> range...

## Finding the Quartiles is just like Finding the Median

1) <u>Quartiles</u> divide the data into <u>four equal groups</u>.
2) The quartiles are the <u>lower quartile $Q_1$</u>, the <u>median $Q_2$</u> and the <u>upper quartile $Q_3$</u>.
3) If you put the data in ascending order, the quartiles are 25% (¼), 50% (½) and 75% (¾) of the way through the list.

**EXAMPLE** Find the value of <u>$Q_1$</u>, <u>$Q_2$</u> and <u>$Q_3$</u> for this set of numbers: 7, 12, 5, 4, 3, 9, 5, 11, 6

*This is discrete data*

1) Put the data in <u>ASCENDING ORDER</u> — 3, 4, 5, 5, 6, 7, 9, 11, 12

2) Work out where the <u>QUARTILES</u> come in the list using the following <u>formulas</u>:

$$Q_1 \text{ position number} = (n + 1)/4$$
$$Q_2 \text{ position number} = 2(n + 1)/4$$
$$Q_3 \text{ position number} = 3(n + 1)/4$$

*n is just the total number of values.*

Step 1: $n = 9$ so $Q_1$ position no. $= (9 + 1)/4 = 2.5$
$Q_2$ position no. $= 2(9 + 1)/4 = 5$
$Q_3$ position no. $= 3(9 + 1)/4 = 7.5$

*If you get "half values", like in this example, find the halfway point of the two numbers either side of this position. This is just like finding the median of an even number of values.*

Step 2:
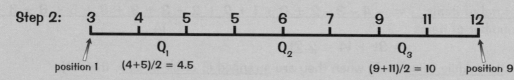

| 3 | 4 | 5 | 5 | 6 | 7 | 9 | 11 | 12 |

$Q_1$ — $(4+5)/2 = 4.5$   $Q_2$   $Q_3$ — $(9+11)/2 = 10$

position 1          position 9

3) So, the lower quartile $Q_1 = 4.5$, the median $Q_2 = 6$ and the upper quartile $Q_3 = 10$.

## Interquartile means "Between Quartiles"

The <u>interquartile range</u> is the <u>difference</u> between the <u>upper quartile</u> and the <u>lower quartile</u>.

**EXAMPLE** Find the <u>interquartile range</u> of the following set of numbers:

*Put the data in ascending order.*  3   4   ④   5   5   6   7   7   ⑨   11   12

Upper quartile = 9   Lower quartile = 4   Interquartile range = 9 – 4 = 5

And for non-grouped data that's all there is to it, but with grouped data it's a bit trickier. You can estimate the interquartile range using a cumulative frequency graph (see p.28).

## The interquartile ranger — fighting crime between quartiles...

This page is really important, so make sure you understand it, then have a go at this question:
1) For the list of integers from 1 to 999 inclusive:
  a) What is the value of the lower quartile?
  b) What is the value of the upper quartile?
2) Write down the odd numbers between 1 and 13 inclusive. What is the interquartile range?

# Frequency Tables

Frequency tables can either be done in <u>rows</u> or in <u>columns</u> of numbers and they can be quite confusing, <u>but not if you learn these eight key points</u>:

## Eight Key Points

1) The word <u>FREQUENCY</u> just means <u>HOW MANY</u>, so a frequency table is nothing more than a '<u>How many in each group</u>' table.

2) The <u>FIRST ROW</u> (or column) just gives the <u>GROUP LABELS</u>.

3) The <u>SECOND ROW</u> (or column) gives the <u>ACTUAL DATA</u>.

4) You have to <u>WORK OUT A THIRD ROW</u> (or column) <u>yourself</u>.

5) The <u>MEAN</u> is always found using:  | 3rd Row Total ÷ 2nd Row Total |

6) The <u>MEDIAN</u> is found from the <u>MIDDLE VALUE in the 2nd row</u>.

7) The <u>INTERQUARTILE RANGE</u> is found from the values ¼ and ¾ of the way through the middle row.

8) The <u>RANGE</u> is found from <u>the extremes of the first row</u>.

## Example

Here is a typical frequency table shown in both <u>ROW FORM</u> and <u>COLUMN FORM</u>:

| No. of Sisters | Frequency |
|:---:|:---:|
| 0 | 7 |
| 1 | 15 |
| 2 | 12 |
| 3 | 8 |
| 4 | 3 |
| 5 | 1 |
| 6 | 0 |

| No. of Sisters | 0 | 1 | 2 | 3 | 4 | 5 | 6 |
|:---:|:---:|:---:|:---:|:---:|:---:|:---:|:---:|
| Frequency | 7 | 15 | 12 | 8 | 3 | 1 | 0 |

Column Form

Row Form

There's no real difference between these two forms and you could get either one in your Exam. Whichever you get, make sure you remember these <u>THREE IMPORTANT FACTS</u>:

1) <u>THE 1ST ROW</u> (or column) gives us the <u>GROUP LABELS</u> for <u>the different categories</u> : i.e. 'no sisters', 'one sister', 'two sisters', etc.

2) <u>THE 2ND ROW</u> (or column) <u>is the ACTUAL DATA</u> and tells us <u>HOW MANY (people) THERE ARE in each category</u> i.e. 7 people had 'no sisters', 15 people had 'one sister', etc.

3) <u>BUT YOU SHOULD SEE THE TABLE AS UNFINISHED</u> because it still needs <u>A THIRD ROW</u> (or column) and <u>TOTALS</u> for the <u>2nd and 3rd rows</u>, as shown on the next page:

# Frequency Tables

And here they are — the <u>completed tables</u> you've been eagerly awaiting...

This is what the two types of table look like when they're completed:

| No. of Sisters | 0 | 1 | 2 | 3 | 4 | 5 | 6 | Totals | |
|---|---|---|---|---|---|---|---|---|---|
| Frequency | 7 | 15 | 12 | 8 | 3 | 1 | 0 | 46 | (People asked) |
| No. × Frequency | 0 | 15 | 24 | 24 | 12 | 5 | 0 | 80 | (Sisters) |

| No. of Sisters | Frequency | No. × Frequency |
|---|---|---|
| 0 | 7 | 0 |
| 1 | 15 | 15 |
| 2 | 12 | 24 |
| 3 | 8 | 24 |
| 4 | 3 | 12 |
| 5 | 1 | 5 |
| 6 | 0 | 0 |
| Totals | 46 | 80 |

(People asked)   (Sisters)

## "WHERE DOES THE THIRD ROW COME FROM?"

....I hear you cry!

<u>THE THIRD ROW</u> (or column) is <u>ALWAYS</u> obtained by <u>MULTIPLYING</u> the numbers from the <u>FIRST 2 ROWS</u> (or columns).

> **THIRD ROW = 1ST ROW × 2ND ROW**

Once the table is complete, you can easily find the <u>MEAN, MEDIAN, MODE AND RANGE</u> (see p.23) which is what they usually demand in the Exam:

Mean sisters

## Mean, Median, Mode and Range:

This is easy enough <u>if you learn it</u>. If you don't, you'll drown in a sea of numbers.

**MEAN** $= \dfrac{\text{3rd Row Total}}{\text{2nd Row Total}} = \dfrac{80}{46} = 1.74$ (sisters per person)

**MEDIAN** — imagine the original data <u>SET OUT IN ASCENDING ORDER</u>:

0000000 111111111111111 222222222222 33333333 444 5

and the median is just the middle number which is between the 23rd and 24th digits.
So for this data <u>THE MEDIAN IS 2</u>. (Of course, when you get slick at this you can easily find the position of the middle value straight from the table)

**The MODE is very easy** — it's just <u>THE GROUP WITH THE MOST ENTRIES</u>: i.e <u>1</u>

**The RANGE is 5 – 0 = <u>5</u>** The 2nd row tells us there are people with anything from 'no sisters' right up to 'five sisters' (but not 6 sisters). (Always give it as a <u>single number</u>.)

---

What's this? No gag? Yes well I thought you might appreciate being able to reach the end of one page without having to endure a pathetic attempt at humour. See, I really do care. Normal service will be resumed on p27. Now learn the <u>8 key points</u> for frequency tables, then turn over and write them down to see what you know.

Using the methods you have just learned and this frequency table, find the MEAN, MEDIAN, MODE and RANGE of the no. of phones that people have.

| No. of phones | 0 | 1 | 2 | 3 | 4 | 5 | 6 |
|---|---|---|---|---|---|---|---|
| Frequency | 1 | 25 | 53 | 34 | 22 | 5 | 1 |

# Grouped Frequency Tables

These are a bit <u>trickier</u>. The table below shows the distribution of weights of 60 school kids:

| Weight | $30 \leq w < 40$ | $40 \leq w < 50$ | $50 \leq w < 60$ | $60 \leq w < 70$ | $70 \leq w < 80$ |
|---|---|---|---|---|---|
| Frequency | 8 | 16 | 18 | 12 | 6 |

## What does $30 \leq w < 40$ mean?

Don't get confused by the notation used for the intervals.

1) the $\leq$ symbol means w can be <u>greater than or equal to 30</u>

2) the $<$ symbol means w must be <u>less than 40</u> (but not equal to it)

So <u>a value of 30</u> will go in this class, but <u>a value of 40</u> will have to go in the next class up: $40 \leq w < 50$.

## 'Estimating' The Mean using Mid-Interval Values

Just like with ordinary frequency tables you have to <u>add extra rows and find totals</u> to be able to work anything out. Also notice <u>you can only 'ESTIMATE' the mean from grouped data tables</u> — you can't find it exactly unless you know all the original values.

> 1) <u>Add a 3rd row</u> and enter the <u>MID-INTERVAL VALUE</u> for each class.
>
> 2) <u>Add a 4th row</u> and <u>multiply FREQUENCY by the MID-INTERVAL VALUE</u> for each class.

| Weight (kg) | $30 \leq w < 40$ | $40 \leq w < 50$ | $50 \leq w < 60$ | $60 \leq w < 70$ | $70 \leq w < 80$ | Totals |
|---|---|---|---|---|---|---|
| Frequency | 8 | 16 | 18 | 12 | 6 | 60 |
| Mid-Interval Value | 35 | 45 | 55 | 65 | 75 | — |
| Frequency × Mid-Interval Value | 280 | 720 | 990 | 780 | 450 | 3220 |

1) <u>ESTIMATING THE MEAN</u> is then the usual thing of <u>DIVIDING THE TOTALS</u>:

$$\text{Mean} = \frac{\text{Overall Total (4th Row)}}{\text{Frequency Total (2nd Row)}} = \frac{3220}{60} = 53.7$$

2) <u>THE MODE</u> is still nice'n'easy: the modal class is $50 \leq w < 60$ kg.

3) <u>THE MEDIAN</u> can't be found exactly but you can say <u>which class it's in</u>. If all the data were put in order, the 30th/31st entries would be in the $50 \leq w < 60$ kg class.

## Mid-interval value — cheap ice-creams...

Learn all the details on this page, then turn over and write down <u>everything</u> you've learned. Good clean fun.

1) Estimate the mean for this table:

| Length L (cm) | $15.5 \leq L < 16.5$ | $16.5 \leq L < 17.5$ | $17.5 \leq L < 18.5$ | $18.5 \leq L < 19.5$ |
|---|---|---|---|---|
| Frequency | 12 | 18 | 23 | 8 |

2) Also state the modal class, and the class that contains the median.

# Cumulative Frequency

## Four Key Points

1) <u>CUMULATIVE FREQUENCY</u> just means <u>ADDING IT UP AS YOU GO ALONG</u>.

2) You have to <u>ADD A THIRD ROW</u> to the table — the <u>RUNNING TOTAL</u> of the 2nd row.

3) <u>When plotting the graph</u>, always plot points <u>using the HIGHEST VALUE in each group</u> (of row 1) with the value from <u>row 3</u>.   i.e.  plot 13 at <u>160</u>, etc. (see below).

4) Cumulative Frequency is always plotted <u>up the side</u> of a graph, not across.

## Example

| Height (cm) | $140 \leq x < 150$ | $150 \leq x < 160$ | $160 \leq x < 170$ | $170 \leq x < 180$ | $180 \leq x < 190$ | $190 \leq x < 200$ | $200 \leq x < 210$ |
|---|---|---|---|---|---|---|---|
| Frequency | 4 | 9 | 20 | 33 | 36 | 15 | 3 |
| Cumulative frequency | 4 (at 150) | 13 (at 160) | 33 (at 170) | 66 (at 180) | 102 (at 190) | 117 (at 200) | 120 (at 210) |

The graph is plotted from these pairs:  (150, 4)  (160, 13)  (170, 33)  (180, 66) etc.

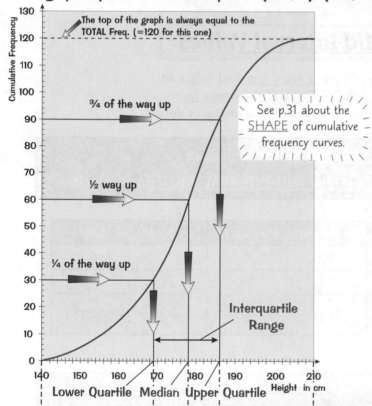

The top of the graph is always equal to the TOTAL Freq. (=120 for this one)

¾ of the way up

½ way up

¼ of the way up

See p.31 about the <u>SHAPE</u> of cumulative frequency curves.

Interquartile Range

Lower Quartile  Median  Upper Quartile

For a cumulative frequency curve there are **THREE VITAL STATISTICS** which you need to know how to find:

1) **MEDIAN**
Exactly <u>halfway UP</u>, then across, then down and <u>read off the bottom scale</u>.

2) **LOWER AND UPPER QUARTILES**
Exactly ¼ and ¾ <u>UP the side</u>, then across, then down and read off the <u>bottom scale</u>.

3) **INTERQUARTILE RANGE**
The distance <u>on the bottom scale</u> between the lower and upper quartiles.

So from the cumulative frequency curve for this data, we get these results:

MEDIAN = <u>178</u> cm
LOWER QUARTILE = <u>169</u> cm
UPPER QUARTILE = <u>186</u> cm
INTERQUARTILE RANGE = <u>17</u> cm   (186-169)

## A Box Plot shows the Inter-Quartile Range as a Box

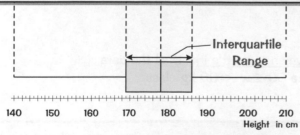

Interquartile Range

To create your very own box plot:
1) <u>Draw the scale</u> along the bottom.
2) <u>Draw a box</u> the length of the <u>interquartile range</u>.
3) <u>Draw a line</u> down the box to show the <u>median</u>.
4) <u>Draw 'whiskers'</u> up to the <u>maximum and minimum</u>.

(They're sometimes called 'Box and Whisker diagrams'.)

## With my cunning plot, I'll soon control all the world's boxes...

Mwahaha.  Learn this page, then cover it up and do these:
Complete this cumulative frequency table.  Draw the graph.
Find the 3 Vital Statistics.  Draw a box plot under the graph.

| No of fish | 41 – 45 | 46 – 50 | 51 – 55 | 56 – 60 | 61 – 65 | 66 – 70 | 71 – 75 |
|---|---|---|---|---|---|---|---|
| Frequency | 2 | 7 | 17 | 25 | 19 | 8 | 2 |

# Histograms and Frequency Density

## Histograms

A histogram is just a bar chart where the bars can be of DIFFERENT widths. This changes them from nice easy-to-understand diagrams into seemingly incomprehensible monsters, and yes, you've guessed it, that makes them a firm favourite with the Examiners.

In fact things aren't half as bad as that — but only if you LEARN THE THREE RULES:

1) It's NOT the height, but the AREA of each bar that matters.

2) Use the snip of information they give you to find how much is represented BY EACH AREA BLOCK.

3) Divide all the bars into THE SAME SIZED AREA BLOCKS and so work out the number for each bar (using AREAS).

**EXAMPLE:** The histogram below represents the age distribution of people arrested for slurping boiled sweets in public places in 1995. Given that there were 36 people in the 55 to 65 age range, find the number of people arrested in all the other age ranges.

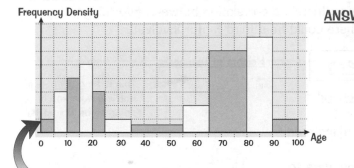

The vertical axis is always called frequency density...

**ANSWER:** The 55-65 bar represents 36 people and contains 4 dotted squares, so each dotted square must represent 9 people.

The rest is easy. E.g. the 80-90 group has 14 dotted squares so that represents $14 \times 9 = 126$ people.

REMEMBER: ALWAYS COUNT AREA BLOCKS to find THE NUMBER IN EACH BAR.

$$\text{Frequency Density} = \text{Frequency} \div \text{Class Width}$$

You don't need to worry too much about this. It says in the specification that you need to understand frequency density, so here it is. Learn the formula and you'll be fine.

## Stem and Leaf Diagrams Use Numbers instead of Bars...

If you get one of these in the exam, you're laughing. It's the EASIEST THING IN THE WORLD.

1) Put the data in order.
2) Put it in groups and make a key.
3) Draw the diagram.

7, 11, 12, 13, 16, 17, 20, 23, 24, 24, 25, 26, 26, 29, 29, 31, 32, 34

This looks like it'll split nicely into tens:

Key: 2 | 3 = 23

Draw a line here.

Put the first digit of each group in a column.

Then put the second digits in rows like this.

```
0 | 7
1 | 1 2 3 6 7
2 | 0 3 4 4 5 6 6 9 9
3 | 1 2 4
```

This one means '26'.

## If stem and leaf diagrams be the food of love, I wanna be single...

Ey up, that was a bit cultured wasn't it. Learn the 3 rules for histograms and for stem and leaf diagrams, then...
1) Find the number of people in each of the age ranges for the histogram above.
2) Draw a stem and leaf diagram for this data: 3, 16, 14, 22, 7, 11, 26, 17, 12, 19, 20, 6, 13, 24, 26

# Scatter Graphs and Bar Charts

## Scatter Graphs — Correlation and the Line of Best Fit

A scatter graph tells you how closely two things are related — the fancy word for this is <u>CORRELATION</u>. <u>Good correlation</u> means the two things are <u>closely related</u> to each other. <u>Poor correlation</u> means there is <u>very little relationship</u>. The <u>LINE OF BEST FIT</u> goes roughly <u>through the middle of the scatter of points</u>. (It doesn't have to go through any of the points exactly but it can.) If the line slopes <u>up</u> it's <u>positive correlation</u>, if it slopes <u>down</u> it's <u>negative correlation</u>. <u>No correlation</u> means there's no <u>linear relationship</u>.

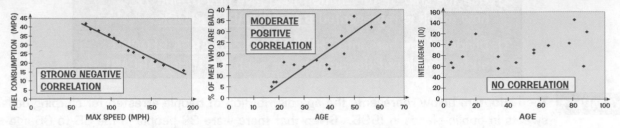

If a change in one variable <u>CAUSES</u> a change in the other variable, they're said to have a <u>CAUSAL LINK</u>. You have to be <u>VERY CAREFUL</u> though. Just because there's a correlation between two things, it <u>doesn't</u> necessarily mean there's a causal link — there could be a <u>third factor</u> involved.

### Outliers don't fit the General Pattern

1) <u>Outliers</u> are data points that <u>don't fit</u> the <u>general pattern</u> (e.g. the 8-foot tall 15-year-old on this graph).
2) Outliers can show <u>possible errors</u> — but outliers aren't <u>necessarily</u> mistakes.
3) If you find one on a graph, <u>check</u> the <u>original data</u> to see whether it's been plotted correctly.

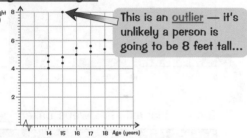

Heights of Teenagers

This is an <u>outlier</u> — it's unlikely a person is going to be 8 feet tall...

## Dual Bar Charts Can be Used to Compare Data Sets

<u>Dual</u> bar charts show <u>two</u> sets of data at once so it's <u>easy to compare them</u>. Each category has two bars — <u>one for each data set</u>.

The dual bar chart on the right shows the favourite colours of a group of pupils, but it's split into two sets — <u>boys</u> and <u>girls</u>.

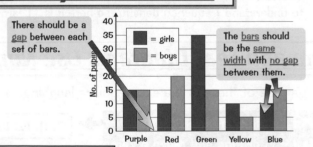

There should be a <u>gap</u> between each set of bars.

The <u>bars</u> should be the <u>same width</u> with <u>no gap</u> between them.

## Composite Bar Charts show Proportions

1) A <u>composite bar chart</u> has <u>single</u> bars, split into <u>sections</u>. The sections show <u>frequencies</u> for the different <u>categories</u> that make up the whole bar.
2) It's easy to read off <u>total frequencies</u> (the <u>heights</u> of the bars), as well as to <u>compare</u> different <u>categories</u>.

The composite bar chart on the right shows the number of men, women and children visiting a county show.

The data might be in <u>percentages</u>, with the height of the whole bar representing 100%.

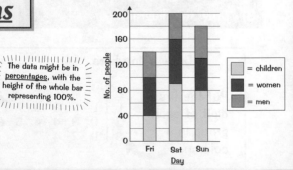

## The data's coming — everybody scatter...

...but before you do, learn the page and answer this question. Ahhhhhhh...

1) a) Use this data to draw and label a scatter diagram.
   b) Draw a line of best fit through the data.
   c) What type of correlation does the data show?

| Average temperature °C | 15 | 21 | 16 | 27 | 8 | 14 | 19 |
|---|---|---|---|---|---|---|---|
| Number of cold drinks sold | 15 | 29 | 19 | 38 | 4 | 16 | 24 |

# Spread of Data

## Averages and 'Spread'

1) AVERAGES can be used to <u>compare</u> sets of data. Take a look at this example:

   **EXAMPLE** Below are the results of Steve's and Sachin's last 10 Physics tests.
   <u>Use these results to say who is better at Physics</u>.

   | <u>Steve</u>: Mean mark = 22.6 | <u>Sachin</u>: Mean mark = 34.4 |
   |---|---|
   | Median mark = 24 | Median mark = 33.5 |
   | Modal mark = 16 | Modal mark = 33 |
   | Range = 18 | Range = 8 |

   <u>ANSWER</u>: Sachin's mean, median and modal marks are all higher than Steve's,
   so "<u>the results suggest that Sachin is better at Physics</u>".

2) The <u>RANGE</u> is used to compare the <u>SPREADS</u> of data. So going back to the example
   — Steve's range of marks is a lot bigger than Sachin's, which means that his
   <u>spread of marks is greater</u>. In other words, <u>Sachin's marks are more consistent</u>.

## Shapes of Histograms and 'Spread'

You can easily estimate the mean from the shape of a histogram — it's more or less <u>IN THE MIDDLE</u>.

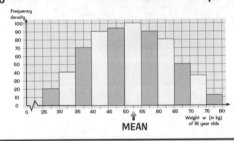

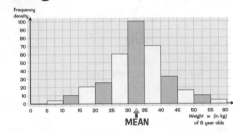

You must <u>LEARN the significance of the shapes</u> of these two histograms:

1) The first shows <u>high dispersion</u> (i.e. a <u>large spread</u> of results away from the mean).
   (i.e. the weights of a sample of 16 year olds will cover a very wide range)

2) The second shows a '<u>tighter</u>' distribution of results where most values are within a <u>narrow range</u>
   either side of the mean. (i.e the weights of a sample of 8 year olds will show <u>very little</u> variation)

## Cumulative Freq. Curves and 'Spread'

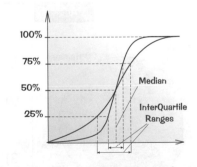

The shape of a <u>CUMULATIVE FREQUENCY CURVE</u> also tells us
<u>how spread out</u> the data values are.

The <u>blue</u> curve shows a <u>very tight distribution</u> around the MEDIAN and
this also means the <u>interquartile range is small</u> as shown.

The <u>red</u> curve shows a more <u>widely spread</u> set of
data and therefore a <u>larger interquartile range</u>.

'Tight' distribution represents <u>CONSISTENT</u> results. E.g. the <u>lifetimes of light bulbs</u> would all be very close
to the median, indicating a <u>good product</u>. The lifetimes of another product may show <u>wide variation</u>, which
shows that the product is not as consistent. They often ask about this 'shape significance' in <u>Exams</u>.

## Data spread — delicious and low in fat...

A nice 'n busy page this one — learn it all, turn over and write down all the <u>important details</u> from memory. Then:
1) Draw two contrasting histograms showing speeds of cyclists and motorists.
2) Sketch two cumulative frequency curves for heights of 5 yr olds and 13 yr olds.

# Other Graphs and Charts

## Two-Way Tables

Two-way <u>tables</u> are a bit like frequency tables, but they show <u>two</u> things instead of just <u>one</u>.

**EXAMPLE:** "Use this table to work out how many
a) <u>right-handed people</u> and
b) <u>left-handed women</u> there were in this survey."

| | Women | Men | TOTAL |
|---|---|---|---|
| Left-handed | | 27 | 63 |
| Right-handed | 164 | 173 | |
| TOTAL | 200 | 200 | 400 |

**ANSWER:**

a) 164 + 173 = <u>337 right-handed people</u> (or you could have done 400 − 63 = 337).

b) 200 − 164 = <u>36 left-handed women</u> (or you could have done 63 − 27 = 36).  Easy.

## Line Graphs and Frequency Polygons

A <u>line graph</u> is just a set of points joined with straight lines.

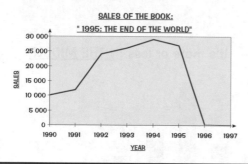

SALES OF THE BOOK:
"1995: THE END OF THE WORLD"

A <u>frequency polygon</u> looks similar and is used to show the information from a frequency table:

| Length l (m) | Frequency |
|---|---|
| $20 \leqslant l < 30$ | 12 |
| $30 \leqslant l < 40$ | 21 |
| $40 \leqslant l < 50$ | 18 |
| $50 \leqslant l < 60$ | 10 |

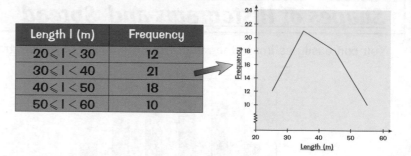

## Pie Charts

Learn the <u>Golden Rule</u> for Pie Charts: **The TOTAL of Everything = 360°**

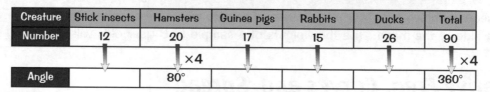

| Creature | Stick insects | Hamsters | Guinea pigs | Rabbits | Ducks | Total |
|---|---|---|---|---|---|---|
| Number | 12 | 20 | 17 | 15 | 26 | 90 |
| Angle | | 80° | | | | 360° |

×4 ... ×4

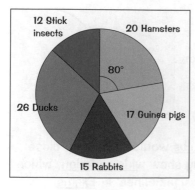

12 Stick insects  20 Hamsters  80°  26 Ducks  17 Guinea pigs  15 Rabbits

1) Add up all the numbers in each sector to get the <u>TOTAL</u> (90 for this one).

2) Then find the <u>MULTIPLIER</u> (or divider) that you need to <u>turn your total into 360°</u>:
For 90 → 360 as above, the <u>MULTIPLIER</u> is 4.

3) Now <u>MULTIPLY EVERY NUMBER BY 4</u> to get the angle for each sector.
E.g. the angle for hamsters will be 20 × 4 = <u>80°</u>.

Pie charts <u>only</u> tell you the <u>proportion</u> of the population that's in each category.
You can't know the <u>actual number</u> of things in a category unless you're told the population size.
This is especially important when you're <u>comparing</u> pie charts.

## I'm a multiplier, twisted multiplier...

Lotsa useful diagrams on this page — learn all the details of the <u>four types of chart</u>.  Got all that stored?  Good...

1) Turn over the page and draw an example of each chart.

2) Work out the angles for all the other animals in the pie chart shown above.

# Basic Algebra

Normally I don't like to be too negative, but sometimes being negative is important...
Negative numbers crop up everywhere so you need to learn this rule for dealing with them:

## Be Careful with Negative Numbers

| + | + makes | + |
| + | – makes | – |
| – | + makes | – |
| – | – makes | + |

Only to be used when:

**1) Multiplying or dividing:**

e.g.  -2 × 3 = <u>-6</u>,    -8 ÷ -2 = <u>+4</u>    -4p × -2 = <u>+8p</u>

**2) Two signs are together:**

e.g.   5 – -4 = 5+4 = <u>9</u>      4 + -6 – -7 = 4 – 6 + 7 = <u>5</u>

## Letters Multiplied Together

Watch out for these combinations of letters in algebra that regularly catch people out:

1)  abc  means a×b×c. The ×'s are often left out to make it clearer.
2)  $gn^2$ means g×n×n. Note that only the n is squared, not the g as well, e.g. $\pi r^2$
3)  $(gn)^2$ means g×g×n×n. The brackets mean that <u>BOTH</u> letters are squared.
4)  $p(q - r)^3$ means p × (q – r) × (q – r) × (q – r). Only the brackets get cubed.
5)  $-3^2$ is a bit ambiguous. It should either be written $(-3)^2 = 9$, or $-(3^2) = -9$

## Expressions, Equations, Formulas and Identities

You need to know the difference between these four things, and be able to spot them all.

1)  <u>EXPRESSION</u>: This is just a bunch of <u>letters</u> and/or <u>numbers</u> added, subtracted, multiplied or divided together. E.g. $y^2$,  2 + 6,  mx + 2,  $3y^3 - 2n$

2)  <u>EQUATION</u>: This is <u>two expressions</u> joined with an <u>equals sign</u>. It says that the two expressions either side of the equals sign have the same value. E.g. $2x^2 = 3x + 2$

3)  <u>FORMULA</u>: This is a <u>relationship</u> or <u>rule</u> for working something out, written in symbols. E.g. A = ½bh (formula for the area of a triangle, p.61) or s = d ÷ t (formula for speed, p.64).

4)  <u>IDENTITY</u>: This is an equation that's true for <u>all values of the variables</u>. E.g. a + b = b + a. It doesn't matter what 'a' and 'b' are — this is always true.

Identities are sometimes written with a ≡ instead of an = sign — you read it as 'is equivalent to'.

## Ahhh algebra, it's as easy as abc, or 2(ab) + c, or something like that...

Learn everything on this page. Now <u>turn over and write it all down</u>. Then do these without a calculator:
1)  a) -4 × -3  b) -4 + -5 + 3  c) (3x + -2x – 4x) ÷ (2+-5)  d) 120 ÷ -40
2)  If m=2 and n=-3 work out: a) $mn^2$  b) $(mn)^3$  c) $m(4+n)^2$  d) $n^3$  e) $3m^2n^3 + 2mn$

# Straight-Line Graphs

If you thought I-spy was a fun game, wait 'til you play 'recognise the straight-line graph from the equation'.

## 1) Horizontal and Vertical lines: 'x = a' and 'y = a'

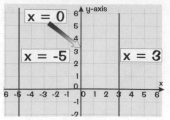 

 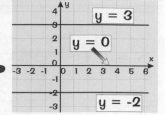

x = a is a vertical line through 'a' on the x-axis

y = a is a horizontal line through 'a' on the y-axis

Don't forget: the y-axis is also the line x=0

Don't forget: the x-axis is also the line y=0

## 2) The Main Diagonals: 'y = x' and 'y = –x'

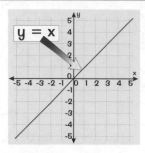 

 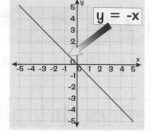

'y = x' is the main diagonal that goes UPHILL from left to right.

'y = -x' is the main diagonal that goes DOWNHILL from left to right.

## 3) Other Sloping Lines Through the origin: 'y = ax' and 'y = –ax'

> y = ax and y = -ax are the equations for **A SLOPING LINE THROUGH THE ORIGIN.**

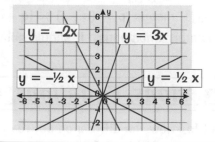

The value of '**a**' (known as the gradient) tells you the steepness of the line. The bigger 'a' is, the steeper the slope. A **MINUS SIGN** tells you it slopes **DOWNHILL**.

## All Other Straight Lines

Other straight-line equations are a little more complicated. The next couple of pages shows you how to read and draw them, but the first step is identifying them in the first place.

Remember: All straight-line equations just contain 'something x, something y, and a number'.

| Straight lines: | | NOT straight lines: | |
|---|---|---|---|
| x – y = 0 | y = 2 + 3x | $y = x^3 + 3$ | 2y – 1/x = 7 |
| 2y – 4x = 7 | 4x – 3 = 5y | 1/y + 1/x = 2 | x(3 – 2y) = 3 |
| 3y + 3x = 12 | 6y – x – 7 = 0 | $x^2 = 4 – y$ | xy + 3 = 0 |

DO NOT PRESS

## My favourite line's y = 3x — it gets the ladies every time...

Ok, so I can't offer a guarantee with that. But it's still worth learning all the graphs on this page and how to identify straight-line equations. Once you think you know it, turn over the page and try and write it all down.

# Straight-Line Graphs

What could be more fun than points in one quadrant? Points in <u>four quadrants</u>, that's what...

## The Four Quadrants

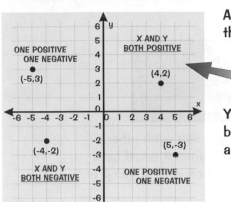

A graph has <u>four different quadrants</u> (regions) where the x- and y- coordinates are either <u>positive</u> or <u>negative</u>.

This is the easiest region by far because here <u>all the coordinates are positive</u>.

You have to be careful in the <u>other regions</u> though, because the x- and y- coordinates could be <u>negative</u>, and that always makes life much more difficult.

Coordinates are always written in brackets like this: **(x, y)** — remember x is <u>across</u>, and y is <u>up</u>.

## Finding the Gradient

### 1) Find **TWO ACCURATE POINTS** and **COMPLETE THE TRIANGLE**

Both points should be in the <u>upper right quadrant</u> if possible (to keep all the numbers positive).

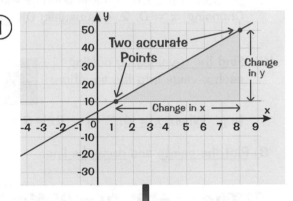

① Two accurate Points

Change in y

Change in x

### 2) Find the **CHANGE IN Y** and the **CHANGE IN X**

Make sure you subtract the x coords. the <u>same way round</u> as you do the y coords.
E.g. y coord. of pt A − y coord. of pt B
<u>and</u> x coord of pt A − x coord of pt B

② <u>Change in y</u> = 50 − 10 = <u>40</u>
<u>Change in x</u> = 8 − 1 = <u>7</u>

### 3) **LEARN** this formula, and use it:

**GRADIENT = CHANGE IN Y / CHANGE IN X**

③ Gradient = $\frac{40}{7}$ = <u>5.7</u>

④ As the graph goes <u>UPHILL</u>, the gradient is positive. So <u>5.7 is correct</u>, not -5.7

### 4) Check the <u>SIGN'S</u> right.

If it slopes <u>UPHILL</u> left → right ( ⟋ ) <u>then it's positive</u>
If it slopes <u>DOWNHILL</u> left → right ( ⟍ ) <u>then it's negative</u>

If you subtracted the coordinates the right way round, the sign should be correct. If it's not, go back and check what you've done.

## Finding gradients is often an uphill battle...

Learn the <u>four steps</u> for finding a gradient then <u>turn over</u> and <u>write them down</u> from memory. Fun times ahoy.
1) Plot these 3 points on a graph: (0,3) (2,0) (5,-4.5) and then join them up with a straight line.
   Now carefully apply the <u>four steps</u> to find the gradient of the line.

# Straight-Line Graphs

Sadly, this isn't about a sinister gang of straight-line graphs, plotting to take over the world. But then that isn't likely to come up in the exam, and <u>drawing straight-line graphs</u> is. There are <u>two</u> methods you can use:

## 1) The 'Table of 3 Values' Method

You can <u>easily</u> draw the graph of <u>any equation</u> using this <u>easy</u> method:

> 1) Choose <u>3 values of x</u> and <u>draw up a wee table</u>,
> 2) <u>Work out the y-values</u>,
> 3) <u>Plot the coordinates</u>, and <u>draw the line</u>.

If it's a <u>straight line equation</u>, the 3 points will be in a <u>dead straight line</u> with each other, which is the usual check you do when you've drawn it — <u>if they aren't</u>, then it could be a <u>curve</u> and you'll need to add <u>more values to your table</u> to find out what on earth's going on.

**EXAMPLE:** "Draw the graph of y = 2x – 3"

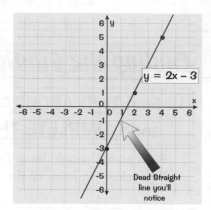

1) <u>Draw up a table</u> with some suitable values of x. Choosing x = 0, 2, 4 is usually OK. i.e.

| x | 0 | 2 | 4 |
|---|---|---|---|
| Y |   |   |   |

2) <u>Find the y-values</u> by putting each x-value into the equation:

| x | 0 | 2 | 4 |
|---|---|---|---|
| Y | –3 | 1 | 5 |

   (e.g. When <u>x = 4</u>,    y = 2x – 3 = 2 × 4 – 3 = <u>5</u> )

3) <u>Plot the points</u> and <u>draw the line</u>.

## 2) The 'x = 0', 'y = 0' Method

> 1) <u>Set x=0</u> in the equation, and <u>find y</u> — this is where it <u>crosses the y-axis</u>.
> 2) <u>Set y=0</u> in the equation and <u>find x</u> — this is where it <u>crosses the x-axis</u>.
> 3) <u>Plot these two points</u> and <u>join them up with a straight line</u> — and just hope it should be a straight line, since with only 2 points you can't really tell, can you!

**EXAMPLE:** "Draw the graph of 5x + 3y = 15"

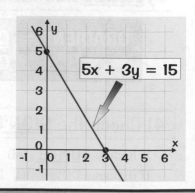

Putting <u>x = 0</u> gives "3y = 15" ⇒ <u>y = 5</u>
Putting <u>y = 0</u> gives "5x = 15" ⇒ <u>x = 3</u>

So plot <u>(0, 5)</u> and <u>(3, 0)</u> on the graph and join them up with a straight line.

   Only doing 2 points is risky unless you're sure the equation is definitely a straight line — but then that's the big thrill of living life on the edge, isn't it.

## ...x set himself to zero. "No!" cried y "I will not let you cross me again"...

I hope you enjoyed that extract from my new book — Methods of a Plotter. It's a psychological thriller about two letters who are bitter enemies. It's almost finished — it just needst a spell check. Now <u>learn</u> the details of these <u>two easy methods</u>, turn over and <u>write down all you know</u>. Then draw these graphs using <u>both</u> methods:
a) y = 4 + x          b) 4y + 3x = 12          c) y = 6 – 2x

# Real-Life Graphs

## Conversion Graphs

These are really easy. In the Exam you're likely to get a conversion graph question which converts between things like £ → Dollars or mph → km/h, etc.

*There's more on converting units on p.63.*

<u>This graph converts between miles and kilometres</u>

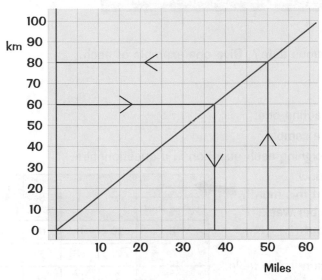

### 2 very typical questions:

**1) How many miles is 60 km?**

ANS: Draw a line <u>straight across</u> from '60' on the 'km' axis 'til it <u>hits the line</u>, then go <u>straight down</u> to the 'miles' axis and read off the answer: <u>37.5 miles</u>

**2) How many km is 50 miles?**

ANS: Draw a line <u>straight up</u> from '50' on the 'miles' axis 'til it <u>hits the line</u>, then go <u>straight across</u> to the 'km' axis and read off the answer: <u>80 km</u>

**METHOD:**

1) <u>Draw a line</u> from the <u>value</u> on one axis.
2) Keep going 'til you <u>hit the LINE</u>.
3) Then <u>change direction</u> and go straight to <u>the other axis</u>.
4) <u>Read off the new value</u> from the axis. <u>That's the answer</u>.

If you remember those 4 simple steps you really can't go wrong — let's face it, conversion graphs are a doddle.

## What the Gradient of a Graph Means

No matter what the graph, <u>THE MEANING OF THE GRADIENT</u> is always simply:

### (y-axis UNITS) PER (x-axis UNITS)

**EXAMPLES:**

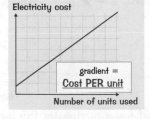
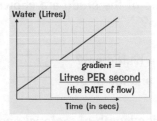
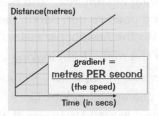
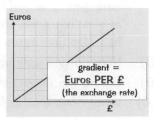

Some gradients have special names like <u>exchange rate</u> or <u>speed</u>, but once you've written down '<u>something PER something</u>' using the y-axis and x-axis <u>UNITS</u>, it's then pretty easy to work out what the gradient represents.

## Right graph — we're not leaving here 'til I get some answers...

<u>Learn</u> the <u>2 simple rules for getting answers</u>, and <u>the meaning of gradient</u>.
Then turn over... bla bla bla ... you know what to do...

*Unit 1 — Statistics and Probability*

# Revision Summary for Unit 1 — Part 2

Here's the really fun page. The inevitable list of straight-down-the-middle questions to test how much you know. Remember, these questions will sort out (quicker than anything else can) exactly what you <u>know</u> and what you <u>don't</u>. And that's exactly what revision is all about, don't forget: <u>find out what you DON'T know</u> and then learn it <u>until you do</u>. Enjoy.

## KEEP LEARNING THESE BASIC FACTS UNTIL YOU KNOW THEM

1) What is primary data? What is secondary data?

2) What is the difference between discrete and continuous data? Give one example of each.

3) What is sampling? What is a sample frame?

4) Describe how to select a simple random sample.

5) What is a stratified sample? Give a method for selecting one.

6) Describe two causes of bias when you're selecting a sample.

7) List three things you need to bear in mind when designing each question in a questionnaire.

8)* Steven works in a shoe shop. His boss wants to know which is the most common size of shoe they've sold this month, and how many of that size they've sold on average per week.
   a) Which two values does Steven need to work out: Mean, Median, Mode or Range?
   b) Work out these two values using the information in the table.

| Size of shoe \ Week | 1 | 2 | 3 | 4 |
|---|---|---|---|---|
| 5 | 29 | 11 | 17 | 12 |
| 6 | 21 | 35 | 7 | 16 |
| 7 | 2 | 17 | 10 | 2 |
| 8 | 15 | 6 | 2 | 2 |

9) How do you work out the lower quartile of a set of data?

10) Write down eight important details about frequency tables.

11)* Jessica's science class are collecting their results in a grouped frequency table. Jessica's result is 5 g. Into which group in the table should her data go?

| Mass (g) | $1 < m \leq 5$ | $5 < m \leq 10$ | $10 < m \leq 15$ |
|---|---|---|---|
| Frequency | 6 | 23 | 5 |

12)* Calum is writing an article on the Skelly Crag half-marathon for the local paper. He wants to include the mean time taken. Estimate the mean time from the table below.

| Time (min) | $60 < t \leq 90$ | $90 < t \leq 120$ | $120 < t \leq 150$ | $150 < t \leq 180$ | $180 < t \leq 210$ | $210 < t \leq 240$ |
|---|---|---|---|---|---|---|
| Frequency | 15 | 60 | 351 | 285 | 206 | 83 |

13) Why is it not possible to find the exact value of the mean from a grouped frequency table?

14) Write down four key points about cumulative frequency.

15) What is a histogram? What are the three steps of the method for tackling all histograms?

16) Write down the formula for frequency density.

17)* A newspaper has claimed that a study shows a strong positive correlation between eating cheese and having nightmares. The results of the study are shown here.
   a) What does strong positive correlation mean?
   b) Do you agree with the newspaper claim?

18) How do you estimate the mean from looking at a histogram?

19) Define the terms: expression, equation, formula and identity.

20) What does a straight line equation look like?

21)* Joe makes curtains for a living. He knows that the length of material needed for a curtain is the length of the window plus one tenth of the length again. He works out the equation $y = x + \frac{1}{10}x$, to show this. He decides to draw a graph so staff can just read the values off that.
   a) Will Joe's graph be a straight line?
   b) Use the 'table of 3 values' method to draw Joe's graph.

22)* Sarah has carried out an experiment to find the rate of photosynthesis at 30°C. Use her graph to calculate how much oxygen is produced per minute.

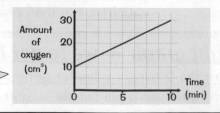

*Unit 1 — Statistics and Probability*     

# Types of Number

A nice easy start to the Unit. I can't promise things won't get harder later on, so enjoy it while you can. :)

## 1) SQUARE NUMBERS:

(1x1) (2x2) (3x3) (4x4) (5x5) (6x6) (7x7) (8x8) (9x9) (10x10) (11x11) (12x12) (13x13) (14x14) (15x15)

| 1 | 4 | 9 | 16 | 25 | 36 | 49 | 64 | 81 | 100 | 121 | 144 | 169 | 196 | 225.. |

3   5   7   9   11   13   15   17   19   21   23   25   27   29

*See p.43 to find out more...*

Note that the <u>DIFFERENCES</u> between the square numbers are all the ODD numbers.

You need to <u>LEARN</u> the first 15 square numbers and make sure you know their <u>SQUARE ROOTS</u> too. You'll be expected to use them in the exam <u>without a calculator</u>.

## 2) CUBE NUMBERS:

They're called <u>CUBE NUMBERS</u> because they're like the volumes of this pattern of cubes.

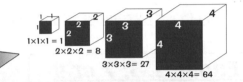

$1\times1\times1 = 1$
$2\times2\times2 = 8$
$3\times3\times3 = 27$
$4\times4\times4 = 64$

| 1 | 8 | 27 | 64 | 125 | 216 | 343 | 512 | 729 | 1000... |

*Admit it, you never knew maths could be this exciting, did you.*

You need to know some of the cube numbers off by heart too — <u>LEARN</u> the cubes of <u>2, 3, 4, 5 and 10</u>.

## 3) POWERS:

Powers are 'numbers <u>multiplied by themselves</u> so many times'.
<u>'Two to the power three'</u> = $2^3 = 2 \times 2 \times 2 = 8$

Here's the first few <u>POWERS OF 2</u>:

| 2 | 4 | 8 | 16 | 32... |

$2^1=2$  $2^2=4$  $2^3=8$  $2^4=16$ etc...

... and the first <u>POWERS OF 10</u> (even easier):

| 10 | 100 | 1000 | 10 000 | 100 000... |

$10^1=10$  $10^2=100$  $10^3=1000$ etc...

## 4) PRIME NUMBERS:

| 2 | 3 | 5 | 7 | 11 | 13 | 17 | 19 | 23 | 29 | 31 | 37 | 41 | 43... |

Prime numbers only divide by themselves and 1 (note that 1 is NOT a prime number).
Apart from 2 and 5, <u>ALL PRIMES END IN 1, 3, 7, OR 9</u>.
So <u>POSSIBLE</u> primes are:     71, 73, 77, 79, ...    101, 103, 107, 109 ....    241, 243, 247, 249 ... etc.
However, <u>not all of these</u> are primes, and working out which are and which aren't is a little bit <u>tricky</u> — see the next page for all the details on how to find prime numbers.

## And there's me thinking numbers were a kind of squiggly shape...

There, that wasn't too bad, was it. Now you need to <u>learn the page</u> — cover it up and <u>write down</u> all the important details. See what you missed and <u>try again</u>.
When you've got it, have a go at this lovely question...

1)  Write down the next five numbers in each of the sequences on this page.

# Types of Number — Prime Numbers

"Hang on a minute," I hear you cry. "We want to know more about them there prime numbers."
Well you're in luck, my poor revising friend...

## 1) Basically, PRIME Numbers don't divide by anything

...and that's the best way to think of them.  (Strictly, they divide by themselves and 1).
So prime numbers are all the numbers that <u>don't</u> come up in times tables:

| 2 | 3 | 5 | 7 | 11 | 13 | 17 | 19 | 23 | 29 | 31 | 37 | ... |

As you can see, they're an awkward-looking bunch (that's because they don't divide by anything!).

For example:

<u>The only numbers</u> that multiply to give 7 are 1 × 7
<u>The only numbers</u> that multiply to give 31 are 1 × 31

In fact the <u>only way</u> to get <u>ANY PRIME NUMBER</u> is 1 × ITSELF

## 2) They End in 1, 3, 7 or 9

1)   1 is <u>NOT</u> a prime number.
2)   The first four prime numbers are  <u>2, 3, 5 and 7</u>.
3)   <u>Prime numbers</u> end in <u>1, 3, 7 or 9</u> (2 and 5 are
      the only exceptions to this rule).
4)   But <u>NOT ALL</u> numbers ending in <u>1, 3, 7 or 9</u> are
      primes, as shown here:
      (Only the <u>circled ones</u> are <u>primes</u>)

(2) (3) (5) (7)
(11) (13) (17) (19)
21 (23) 27 (29)
(31) 33 (37) 39
(41) (43) (47) 49
51 (53) 57 (59)
(61) 63 (67) 69

## 3) How to FIND Prime Numbers – a very simple method

1)   <u>Since all primes</u> (above 5) <u>end in 1, 3, 7, or 9</u>, then to find a prime number
      between say, 70 and 80, <u>the only possibilities</u> are:   <u>71, 73, 77 and 79</u>

2)   Now, to find which of them <u>ACTUALLY ARE</u> primes you only need to <u>divide</u>
      <u>each one by 3 and 7</u>.  If it doesn't divide exactly by either 3 or 7 then it's a prime.
               (This simple rule <u>using just 3 and 7</u> is true for checking primes <u>up to 120</u>)

So, to find the primes between 70 and 80, just try dividing <u>71, 73, 77 and 79</u> by <u>3 and 7</u>:

$71 \div 3 = 23.667$          $71 \div 7 = 10.143$      so <u>71 IS a prime number</u>
                                                    (because it ends in 1, 3, 7 or 9 and it <u>doesn't divide by 3 or 7</u>)

$73 \div 3 = 24.333$          $73 \div 7 = 10.429$     so <u>73 IS a prime number</u>

$79 \div 3 = 26.333$          $79 \div 7 = 11.286$     so <u>79 IS a prime number</u>

$77 \div 3 = 25.667$     <u>BUT</u>:   $77 \div 7 = \underline{11}$ — 11 is a <u>whole number</u> (or 'integer'),
                                                    so <u>77 is NOT a prime</u>, because it <u>divides by 7</u>.

## Two's an odd prime — it's even, which makes it odd.  Hmm...

OK, as before <u>learn</u> all the main points on the page, then <u>cover it up and write it all down</u>.  Then try these...
1)   Write down the first 15 prime numbers (without looking them up).
2)   Find all the prime numbers between 100 and 110.

# Multiples, Factors and Prime Factors

I'm afraid it's time for some good ol' fashioned <u>maths terms</u>. It was bound to happen sooner or later...

## Multiples

| The <u>MULTIPLES</u> of a number are simply its <u>TIMES TABLE</u>: |

So the <u>multiples of 13</u> are... 13  26  39  52  65  78  91  104 ...

## Factors

| The <u>FACTORS</u> of a number are all the numbers that <u>DIVIDE INTO IT</u>. |

There's a special method which guarantees you find them <u>ALL</u>...

**EXAMPLE 1:** "Find all the factors of 24."

1) Start off with 1 × the number itself, then try 2 ×, then 3 × and so on, listing the pairs in rows like this.

2) Try each one in turn, putting a dash if it doesn't divide exactly.

3) Eventually, when you get a number <u>REPEATED</u>, you <u>STOP</u>.

4) So the <u>FACTORS OF 24</u> are <u>1,2,3,4,6,8,12,24</u>

*Increasing by 1 each time*

$1 \times 24$
$2 \times 12$
$3 \times 8$
$4 \times 6$
$5 \times -$
$6 \times 4$

**EXAMPLE 2:** "Find all the factors of 64."

1) <u>Check each one in turn</u>, to see if it divides or not.

2) So the <u>FACTORS of 64</u> are <u>1,2,4,8,16,32,64</u>

$1 \times 64$
$2 \times 32$
$3 \times -$
$4 \times 16$
$5 \times -$
$6 \times -$
$7 \times -$
$8 \times 8$

The 8 has <u>repeated</u> so <u>stop here</u>.

## Finding Prime Factors — The Factor Tree

1) <u>Any number</u> can be broken down into a string of prime numbers all multiplied together — this is called '<u>Expressing it as a product of prime factors</u>', and to be honest it's pretty tedious — but it's in the Exam.

2) The mildly entertaining '<u>Factor Tree</u>' method is best, where you start at the top and split your number off into factors as shown.

3) Each time you get a prime you <u>ring it</u> and you finally end up with all the prime factors, which you can then arrange in order.

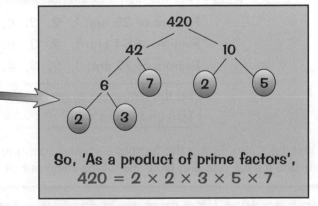

So, 'As a product of prime factors',
$420 = 2 \times 2 \times 3 \times 5 \times 7$

## Takes me back to my youth, scrumping prime factors from the orchards...

...innocent times, they were. Right, learn how to find <u>multiples, factors and prime factors</u> and do these Qs:

1) List the first 10 multiples of 7.

2) List all the factors of 36 and all the factors of 84.

3) Express as a product of prime factors:   a) 990   b) 160.

# LCM and HCF

Two big fancy names but don't be put off — they're both <u>real easy</u>.

## LCM — 'Lowest Common Multiple'

'Lowest Common Multiple' — sure, it sounds kind of complicated but all it means is this:

> The <u>SMALLEST</u> number that will <u>DIVIDE BY ALL</u> the numbers in question.

**METHOD:**
1) <u>LIST</u> the <u>MULTIPLES</u> of <u>ALL</u> the numbers.
2) Find the <u>SMALLEST</u> one that's in <u>ALL the lists</u>.
3) Easy peasy innit.

**EXAMPLE:** Find the lowest common multiple (LCM) of 6 and 7

Multiples of 6 are: 6, 12, 18, 24, 30, 36, (42,) 48, 54, 60, 66, ...
Multiples of 7 are: 7, 14, 21, 28, 35, (42,) 49, 56, 63, 70, 77, ...

> So the <u>lowest common multiple</u> (LCM) of 6 and 7 is <u>42</u>.
> Told you it was easy.

## HCF — 'Highest Common Factor'

'Highest Common Factor' — all it means is <u>this</u>:

> The <u>BIGGEST</u> number that will <u>DIVIDE INTO ALL</u> the numbers in question.

**METHOD:**
1) <u>LIST</u> the <u>FACTORS</u> of <u>ALL</u> the numbers.
2) Find the <u>BIGGEST</u> one that's in <u>ALL the lists</u>.
3) Easy peasy innit.

**EXAMPLE:** Find the highest common factor (HCF) of 36, 54, and 72

Factors of 36 are: 1, 2, 3, 4, 6, 9, 12, (18,) 36
Factors of 54 are: 1, 2, 3, 6, 9, (18,) 27, 54
Factors of 72 are: 1, 2, 3, 4, 6, 8, 9, 12, (18,) 24, 36, 72

> So the <u>highest common factor</u> (HCF) of 36, 54 and 72 is <u>18</u>.
> Told you it was easy.

Just <u>take care</u> listing the factors — make sure you use the <u>proper method</u> (as shown on the previous page) or you'll miss one and blow the whole thing out of the water.

## _I wanna live like common factors. I wanna do whatever common factors do..._

I wanna sle... actually, best not go there. You need to learn what LCM and HCF are, and <u>how to find them</u>. Turn over and write it all down. And after that, some lovely questions — Bonus.

1) List the first 10 multiples of 8, and the first 10 multiples of 9. What's their LCM?
2) List <u>all</u> the factors of 56 and <u>all</u> the factors of 104. What's their HCF?
3) What's the Lowest Common Multiple of 7 and 9?
4) What's the Highest Common Factor of 36 and 84?

# Powers and Roots

**Powers are a very useful shorthand:** $2 \times 2 \times 2 \times 2 \times 2 \times 2 \times 2 = 2^7$ ('two to the power 7')

That bit is easy to remember. Unfortunately, there are <u>ten special rules</u> for powers that are not tremendously exciting, but you do need to know them for the Exam:

## The Seven Easy Rules:

The first two only work for powers of the same number.

1) When <u>MULTIPLYING</u>, you <u>ADD THE POWERS</u>.    e.g. $3^4 \times 3^6 = 3^{6+4} = 3^{10}$

2) When <u>DIVIDING</u>, you <u>SUBTRACT THE POWERS</u>.    e.g. $5^4 \div 5^2 = 5^{4-2} = 5^2$

3) When <u>RAISING</u> one power to another, you <u>MULTIPLY THEM</u>.   e.g. $(3^2)^4 = 3^{2 \times 4} = 3^8$

4) $X^1 = X$, <u>ANYTHING</u> to the <u>POWER 1</u> is just <u>ITSELF</u>.    e.g. $3^1 = 3$, $6 \times 6^3 = 6^4$

5) $X^0 = 1$, <u>ANYTHING</u> to the <u>POWER 0</u> is just <u>ONE</u>.    e.g. $5^0 = 1$    $67^0 = 1$

6) $1^x = 1$, <u>1 TO ANY POWER</u> is <u>STILL JUST 1</u>.    e.g. $1^{23} = 1$   $1^{89} = 1$   $1^2 = 1$

7) <u>FRACTIONS</u> — Apply power to <u>both TOP and BOTTOM</u>.   e.g. $\left(1\frac{3}{5}\right)^3 = \left(\frac{8}{5}\right)^3 = \frac{8^3}{5^3} = \frac{512}{125}$

## The Three Tricky Rules:

8) <u>NEGATIVE Powers</u> — Turn it Upside-Down

People do have quite a bit of difficulty remembering this.

Whenever you see a negative power you're supposed to immediately think:
"Aha, that means turn it the other way up and make the power positive"

Like this: e.g. $7^{-2} = \frac{1}{7^2} = \frac{1}{49}$    $\left(\frac{3}{5}\right)^{-2} = \left(\frac{5}{3}\right)^{+2} = \frac{5^2}{3^2} = \frac{25}{9}$

9) <u>FRACTIONAL POWERS</u>

> The power $\frac{1}{2}$ means <u>Square Root</u>,
> The power $\frac{1}{3}$ means <u>Cube Root</u>,
> The power $\frac{1}{4}$ means <u>Fourth Root</u> etc.

e.g. $25^{1/2} = \sqrt{25} = 5$
$64^{1/3} = \sqrt[3]{64} = 4$
$81^{1/4} = \sqrt[4]{81} = 3$ etc.

The one to really watch is when you get a <u>negative fraction</u> like $49^{-1/2}$ — people get mixed up and think that the minus is the square root, and forget to turn it upside down as well.

10) <u>TWO-STAGE FRACTIONAL POWERS</u>

They really like putting these in Exam questions so learn the method:
With fractional powers like $64^{5/6}$ always <u>split the fraction</u> into a <u>root</u> and a <u>power</u>, and do them in that order: <u>root</u> first, then <u>power</u>: $(64)^{1/6 \times 5} = (64^{1/6})^5 = (2)^5 = 32$

## Square Roots can be Positive or Negative

Whenever you take the square root of a number, the answer can be <u>positive</u> or <u>negative</u>...

E.g. $x^2 = 4$ gives $x = \pm\sqrt{4} = +2$ or $-2$    You always get a <u>+ve</u> and <u>−ve</u> version of the <u>same number</u> (your calculator only gives the +ve answer).

The reason for it becomes clear when you work backwards by squaring the answers:
$2^2 = 2 \times 2 = 4$   but also   $(-2)^2 = (-2) \times (-2) = 4$

## Square Roots? Must be a geomer-tree...*

Learn all <u>ten exciting rules</u> on this page. Then turn over and write them all down with <u>examples</u>. <u>Keep trying till you can</u>.

1) Simplify:   a) $3^2 \times 3^6$   b) $4^3/4^2$   c) $(8^3)^4$   d) $(3^2 \times 3^3 \times 1^6)/3^5$   e) $7^3 \times 7 \times 7^2$

2) Evaluate   a) $(1/4)^{-3}$   b) $25^{-2}$   c) $25^{-1/2}$   d) $(27/216)^{-1/3}$   e) $625^{3/4}$

*winner of Best Maths Gag in a Supporting Role,
International Algebra Awards 2010

# Standard Index Form

Standard form (or 'standard index form') is only really useful for writing <u>VERY BIG</u> or <u>VERY SMALL</u> numbers in a more convenient way,  e.g.

56 000 000 000 would be $5.6 \times 10^{10}$ in standard form.

0.000 000 003 45 would be $3.45 \times 10^{-9}$ in standard form.

But <u>ANY NUMBER</u> can be written in standard form and you need to know how to do it:

## What it Actually is:

A number written in standard form must <u>ALWAYS</u> be in <u>EXACTLY</u> this form:

$$A \times 10^n$$

This <u>number</u> must <u>always</u> be <u>BETWEEN 1 AND 10</u>.

(The fancy way of saying this is:  $1 \leq A < 10$ — they sometimes write that in Exam questions — don't let it put you off, just remember what it means).

This number is just the <u>NUMBER OF PLACES</u> the <u>Decimal Point</u> moves.

## Learn The Three Rules:

1) The <u>front number</u> must always be <u>BETWEEN 1 AND 10</u>.

2) The power of 10, n, is purely: <u>HOW FAR THE D.P. MOVES</u>.

3) n is <u>+ve</u> for <u>BIG</u> numbers, n is <u>−ve</u> for <u>SMALL</u> numbers.

(This is much better than rules based on which way the D.P. moves.)

## Two Very Simple Examples:

1) "Express 35 600 in standard form."

<u>METHOD:</u>

1) Move the D.P. until 35 600 becomes 3.56 ('$1 \leq A < 10$')
2) The D.P. has moved 4 places so n=4, giving: $10^4$
3) 35 600 is a BIG number so n is +4, not −4

<u>ANSWER:</u>

3.5 6 0 0

$= \underline{3.56 \times 10^4}$

2) "Express 0.0000623 in standard form."

<u>METHOD:</u>

1) The D.P. must move <u>5 places to give 6.23</u> ('$1 \leq A < 10$'),
2) So the power of 10 is 5
3) Since 0.0000623 is a <u>SMALL NUMBER</u> it must be $10^{-5}$ not $10^{+5}$.

<u>ANSWER:</u>

0.0 0 0 0 6 2 3

$= \underline{6.23 \times 10^{-5}}$

# Fractions and Decimals

You might think that a decimal is just a decimal. But oh no — things get a lot more juicy than that...

## Recurring or Terminating...

1) <u>Recurring</u> decimals have a <u>pattern</u> of numbers which repeats forever, e.g. $\frac{1}{3}$ is the decimal 0.333333...
   Note, it doesn't have to be a single digit that repeats. You could have, for instance: 0.143143143....

2) <u>Terminating</u> decimals are <u>finite</u>, e.g $\frac{1}{20}$ is the decimal 0.05.

The <u>denominator</u> (bottom number) of a fraction, tells you if it'll be a <u>recurring</u> or <u>terminating</u>
<u>decimal</u> when you convert it. Fractions where the denominator has <u>prime factors</u> of <u>only 2</u>
<u>or 5</u> will give <u>terminating decimals</u>. All <u>other fractions</u> will give <u>recurring decimals</u>.

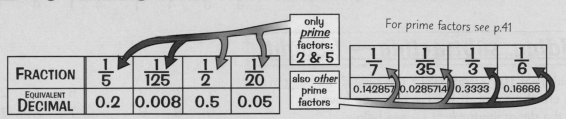

only <u>prime</u> factors: **2 & 5**

also <u>other</u> prime factors

For prime factors see p.41

| FRACTION | $\frac{1}{5}$ | $\frac{1}{125}$ | $\frac{1}{2}$ | $\frac{1}{20}$ | | $\frac{1}{7}$ | $\frac{1}{35}$ | $\frac{1}{3}$ | $\frac{1}{6}$ |
|---|---|---|---|---|---|---|---|---|---|
| EQUIVALENT DECIMAL | 0.2 | 0.008 | 0.5 | 0.05 | | 0.142857 | 0.0285714 | 0.3333 | 0.16666 |

You should have worked out from the previous page the easy method for converting <u>terminating decimals</u>
into fractions — you basically just divide by a <u>power of 10</u> depending on the number of digits after the
decimal point. Converting <u>recurring decimals</u> isn't much harder once you've learnt the method...

## Recurring Decimals into Fractions

There's two ways to do it:  1) by <u>UNDERSTANDING</u>    2) by just <u>LEARNING THE RESULT</u>.

### The Understanding Method:

1) Find the <u>length</u> of the <u>repeating sequence</u> and <u>multiply</u> by 10, 100, 1000, 10 000
   or whatever to move it all up past the decimal point by <u>one full repeated lump</u>:
   E.g.  0.234234234... × 1000  =  234.234234...

2) <u>Subtract the original number</u>, r, from the new one (which in this case is 1000r )
   i.e. 1000r − r = 234.234234... − 0.234234... giving:   999r = 234

3) Then just <u>DIVIDE</u> to leave r:    $r = \frac{234}{999}$ , and cancel if possible: $r = \frac{26}{111}$

### The 'Just Learning The Result' Method:

The fraction always has the repeating unit on the top and the same number of nines on the bottom
— easy as that. Look at these and marvel at the elegant simplicity of it.

$$0.4444444 = \frac{4}{9} \qquad 0.34343434 = \frac{34}{99}$$

$$0.124124124 = \frac{124}{999} \qquad 0.14561456 = \frac{1456}{9999}$$

Always check if it will <u>CANCEL DOWN</u> of course, e.g. $0.363636... = \frac{36}{99} = \frac{4}{11}$.

## Oh, what's recurrin'?...

Learn how to tell whether a fraction will be a <u>terminating or recurring decimal</u>, and all the <u>methods above</u>.
Then turn over and write it all down. Now, try and answer these beauties...

1) Express 0.142857142857... as a fraction.

2) Without cheating, say if these fractions will give recurring or terminating decimals: a) $\frac{3}{8}$   b) $\frac{9}{280}$   c) $\frac{7}{250}$

# Fractions and Decimals

This page shows you how to cope with fraction calculations without your <u>beloved calculator</u>.
For some tricks on doing fractions with your calculator, see p.3.

## 1) Multiplying — easy

Multiply top and bottom separately:

$$\frac{3}{5} \times \frac{4}{7} = \frac{3 \times 4}{5 \times 7} = \frac{12}{35}$$

## 2) Dividing — quite easy

Turn the 2nd fraction <u>UPSIDE DOWN</u> and then <u>multiply</u>:

$$\frac{3}{4} \div \frac{1}{3} = \frac{3}{4} \times \frac{3}{1} = \frac{3 \times 3}{4 \times 1} = \frac{9}{4}$$

## 3) Adding, subtracting — fraught

Add or subtract <u>TOP LINES ONLY</u> but <u>only</u> if the <u>bottom numbers</u> are the same. If they're not, you have to equalise the denominator first — see below.

$$\frac{2}{6} + \frac{1}{6} = \frac{3}{6} \qquad \frac{5}{7} - \frac{3}{7} = \frac{2}{7}$$

## 4) Cancelling down — easy

<u>Divide top and bottom by the same number</u>, till they won't go any further:

$$\overset{\div 3 \quad \div 2}{\frac{18}{24} = \frac{6}{8} = \frac{3}{4}}_{\div 3 \quad \div 2}$$

## 5) Finding a fraction of something — just multiply

<u>Multiply</u> the 'something' by the <u>TOP</u> of the fraction, then <u>divide</u> it by the <u>BOTTOM</u>:

$$\frac{9}{20} \text{ of } £360 = (9 \times £360) \div 20 = \frac{£3240}{20} = £162$$

## 6) Equalising the Denominator

This comes in handy for ordering fractions by size, and for adding or subtracting fractions.
You need to find a common multiple of all the denominators:

> **Example:** Put these fractions in ascending order of size: $\dfrac{8}{3}, \dfrac{6}{4}, \dfrac{12}{5}$
>
> Lowest Common Multiple of 3, 4 and 5 is 60 $\Longrightarrow \dfrac{8}{3} = \dfrac{8}{3} \times \dfrac{20}{20} = \dfrac{160}{60}$
>
> so put all the fractions over 60... $\dfrac{6}{4} = \dfrac{6}{4} \times \dfrac{15}{15} = \dfrac{90}{60}$
>
> $\dfrac{12}{5} = \dfrac{12}{5} \times \dfrac{12}{12} = \dfrac{144}{60}$
>
> So the correct order is $\dfrac{90}{60}, \dfrac{144}{60}, \dfrac{160}{60}$ i.e. $\dfrac{6}{4}, \dfrac{12}{5}, \dfrac{8}{3}$

## No fractions were harmed in the making of this page...

Try all of the following <u>without</u> a calculator.

1) a) $\frac{3}{8} \times \frac{5}{12}$  b) $\frac{4}{5} \div \frac{7}{8}$  c) $\frac{3}{4} + \frac{2}{5}$  d) $\frac{2}{5} - \frac{3}{8}$  e) $4\frac{1}{9} + 2\frac{2}{27}$

2) a) Find $\frac{2}{5}$ of 550.  b) What's $\frac{7}{8}$ of £2?

# Manipulating Surds and Use of π

**RATIONAL NUMBERS** Most numbers you deal with are rational. They can always be written as <u>fractions</u>. You'll come across them in 3 different forms:

1) A <u>whole number</u> (either positive (+ve), or negative (–ve)), e.g. 4 $(=\frac{4}{1})$, -5 $(=\frac{-5}{1})$, -12 $(=\frac{-12}{1})$

2) A <u>fraction</u> p/q, where p and q are whole numbers (+ve or –ve ), e.g. $\frac{1}{4}$, $-\frac{1}{2}$, $\frac{3}{4}$

3) A <u>terminating or recurring decimal</u>, e.g. 0.125 $(=\frac{1}{8})$, 0.3333333333... $(=\frac{1}{3})$, 0.143143143... $(=\frac{143}{999})$

**IRRATIONAL NUMBERS** are messy! They <u>can't</u> be written as fractions

1) They are always <u>never-ending non-repeating decimals</u>. π is irrational.

2) A good source of irrational numbers is <u>square roots</u> and <u>cube roots</u>.

## Manipulating Surds — 7 Rules to Learn

Surds are expressions with irrational square roots in them. You <u>MUST USE THEM</u> if they ask you for an <u>EXACT</u> answer. There's 7 rules you need to learn...

1) $\sqrt{a} \times \sqrt{b} = \sqrt{a \times b}$     e.g. $\sqrt{2} \times \sqrt{3} = \sqrt{2 \times 3} = \sqrt{6}$     — also $(\sqrt{b})^2 = b$, fairly obviously

2) $\frac{\sqrt{a}}{\sqrt{b}} = \sqrt{\frac{a}{b}}$     e.g. $\frac{\sqrt{8}}{\sqrt{2}} = \sqrt{\frac{8}{2}} = \sqrt{4} = 2$

3) $\sqrt{a} + \sqrt{b}$ — <u>DO NOTHING</u> ... (in other words it is definitely NOT $\sqrt{a+b}$ )

4) $(a + \sqrt{b})^2 = (a + \sqrt{b})(a + \sqrt{b}) = a^2 + 2a\sqrt{b} + b$ (NOT just $a^2 + (\sqrt{b})^2$)

5) $(a + \sqrt{b})(a - \sqrt{b}) = a^2 + a\sqrt{b} - a\sqrt{b} - (\sqrt{b})^2 = a^2 - b$

6) Express $\frac{3}{\sqrt{5}}$ in the form $\frac{a\sqrt{5}}{b}$ where a and b are whole numbers.

To do this you must '<u>RATIONALISE the denominator</u>', which just means multiplying top and bottom by $\sqrt{5}$:   $\frac{3\sqrt{5}}{\sqrt{5}\sqrt{5}} = \frac{3\sqrt{5}}{5}$ so a = 3 and b = 5

7) If you want an <u>exact</u> answer, <u>LEAVE THE SURDS IN</u>.

As soon as you go using that calculator, you'll get a <u>big fat rounding error</u> — and you'll get the answer <u>WRONG</u>. Don't say I didn't warn you...

You might have to do this in Pythagoras questions — see p.87.

> **Example:** "A square has an area of 15 cm². Find the length of one of its sides."
> **Answer:** The length of a side is $\sqrt{15}$ cm.
> If you <u>have a calculator</u>, then you can work out $\sqrt{15} = 3.8729833...$cm.
> If you're working <u>without a calculator</u>, or are asked to give an <u>EXACT</u> answer, then just write: $\sqrt{15}$ cm. That's all you have to do.

## Exact calculations using π — Leave π in the answer

π is an <u>irrational</u> number that often comes up in calculations, e.g. in finding the area of a circle (p.102). Most of the time you can use the nifty little π button on your calculator. But if you're asked to give an <u>exact</u> answer or, worse still, do the calculation <u>without a calculator</u>, just <u>leave</u> the π symbol in the calculation.

> **Example:** Find the area of a circle with radius 4 cm, without using a calculator.
> **Answer:** The area $= \pi r^2 = \pi \times 4^2 = 16\pi$ cm².

## Rationalise the denominator? How absurd...

Learn the <u>7 rules</u> for <u>manipulating surds</u>, then turn over and <u>write them all down</u>. Now have a go at these two...

Simplify 1) $(1 + \sqrt{2})^2 - (1 - \sqrt{2})^2$     2) $(1 + \sqrt{2})^2 - (2\sqrt{2} - \sqrt{2})^2$
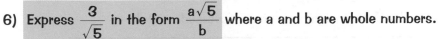

# More Algebra

The next two pages have some really important algebra rules. You'll find yourself using these at least once a day for the rest of your lives*, so it's a good idea to learn them now rather than struggling later on...

## 1) Simplifying or 'Collecting Like Terms'

<u>EXAMPLE</u>: Simplify $2x - 4 + 5x + 6$

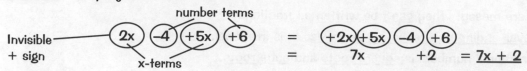

number terms

Invisible + sign
$2x$  $-4$  $+5x$  $+6$ = $+2x$ $+5x$ $-4$ $+6$
x-terms
= $7x$ $+2$ = $\underline{7x + 2}$

1) Put <u>bubbles</u> round each term — be sure you capture the $+/-$ sign in front of each.
2) Then you can move the bubbles into the <u>best order</u> so that <u>like terms</u> are together.
3) "<u>Like terms</u>" have exactly the same combination of letters, e.g. x-terms or xy-terms.
4) <u>Combine like terms</u> using the number line (not the other rule for negative numbers).

## 2) Multiplying out Brackets

1) The thing <u>outside</u> the brackets multiplies <u>each separate term</u> inside the brackets.
2) When letters are multiplied together, they are just written next to each other, pq.
3) Remember, $R \times R = R^2$, and $TY^2$ means $T \times Y \times Y$, whilst $(TY)^2$ means $T \times T \times Y \times Y$.
4) Remember a minus outside the bracket <u>REVERSES ALL THE SIGNS</u> when you multiply.

1) $3(2x + 5) = \underline{6x + 15}$       2) $4p(3r - 2t) = \underline{12pr - 8pt}$
3) $-4(3p^2 - 7q^3) = -12p^2 + 28q^3$ (note both signs have been reversed — Rule 4)

5) <u>DOUBLE BRACKETS</u> — you get <u>4 terms</u>, and usually 2 of them combine to leave <u>3 terms</u>.

$(2P - 4)(3P + 1)$ = $(2P \times 3P) + (2P \times 1) + (-4 \times 3P) + (-4 \times 1)$
= $6P^2$ + $2P$    $-12P$    $-4$
= $\underline{6P^2 - 10P - 4}$    (these 2 combine together)

6) <u>SQUARED BRACKETS</u> — Always write these out as <u>TWO BRACKETS</u>:

E.g. $(3d + 5)^2$ should be written out as $(3d + 5)(3d + 5)$ and then worked out as above.
YOU SHOULD ALWAYS GET <u>FOUR</u> TERMS from a pair of brackets.
The usual <u>WRONG ANSWER</u> is $(3d + 5)^2 = 9d^2 + 25$ (eeek)
It should be: $(3d + 5)^2 = (3d + 5)(3d + 5) = 9d^2 + 15d + 15d + 25 = \underline{9d^2 + 30d + 25}$

## 3) D.O.T.S. — The Difference Of Two Squares:

$$a^2 - b^2 = (a + b)(a - b)$$

The 'difference of two squares' (D.O.T.S. for short) is where you have 'one thing squared' take away 'another thing squared'. Too many people have more trouble than they should with this, probably because they don't make enough effort to learn it as a separate item in its own right. Best learn it now, eh.

1) Factorise $9P^2 - 16Q^2$. Answer: $9P^2 - 16Q^2 = (3P + 4Q)(3P - 4Q)$
2) Factorise $1 - T^4$.       Answer: $1 - T^4 = (1 + T^2)(1 - T^2)$
3) Factorise $3K^2 - 75H^2$. Answer: $3K^2 - 75H^2 = 3(K^2 - 25H^2) = 3(K + 5H)(K - 5H)$

# More Algebra

## 4) Factorising — putting brackets in

This is the exact reverse of multiplying-out brackets. Here's the method to follow:

1) Take out the biggest number that goes into all the terms.
2) Take each letter in turn and take out the highest power (e.g. x, $x^2$ etc) that will go into EVERY term.
3) Open the brackets and fill in all the bits needed to reproduce each term.

EXAMPLE:  Factorise  $15x^4y + 20x^2y^3z - 35x^3yz^2$

Answer:  $5x^2y(3x^2 + 4y^2z - 7xz^2)$

Biggest number that'll divide into 15, 20 and 35.

Highest powers of x and y that will go into all three terms.

z was not in ALL terms so it can't come out as a common factor.

REMEMBER:  The bits taken out and put at the front are the common factors.
The bits inside the brackets are what's needed to get back to the original terms if you multiply the brackets out again.

## 5) Algebraic Fractions

The basic rules are exactly the same as for ordinary fractions.

I love algebraic fractions.

### 1) Multiplying (easy)

Multiply top and bottom separately and cancel if possible:

$$\text{e.g.} \quad \frac{st}{10w^3} \times \frac{35s^2tw}{6} = \frac{35s^3t^2w}{60w^3} = \frac{7s^3t^2}{12w^2}$$

### 2) Dividing (easy)

Turn the second one upside down, then multiply and cancel if possible:

$$\text{e.g.} \quad \frac{12}{p+4} \div \frac{4(p-3)}{3(p+4)} = \frac{\cancel{12}^{3}}{\cancel{p+4}} \times \frac{3\cancel{(p+4)}}{\cancel{4}(p-3)} = \frac{9}{p-3}$$

### 3) Adding/subtracting (not so easy)

Always get a common denominator, i.e. same bottom line (by cross-multiplying) and then ADD TOP LINES ONLY:

$$\frac{t-2p}{3t-p} - \frac{1}{3} = \frac{3(t-2p)}{3(3t-p)} - \frac{1(3t-p)}{3(3t-p)} = \frac{3t-6p-3t+p}{3(3t-p)} = \frac{-5p}{3(3t-p)}$$

## Go forth and multiply out brackets...

Learn the details of all 5 sections on these two pages. Then get your nimble math brains around these:

1) Simplify: $5x + 3y - 4 - 2y - x$
2) Expand $2pq(3p - 4q^2)$
3) Expand $(2g + 5)(4g - 2)$
4) Factorise $14x^2y^3 + 21xy^2 - 35x^3y^4$
5) Simplify $\frac{5abc^3}{18de} \div \frac{15abd^2}{9ce}$
6) Simplify $\frac{3}{5} + \frac{5g}{3g-4}$

# Factorising Quadratics

There are several ways of solving quadratic equations, but you don't need to know about most of them until Unit 3. For Unit 2, you just need to know how to factorise a quadratic.

## Factorising a Quadratic

'Factorising a quadratic' means 'putting it into 2 brackets'.

(There are several different methods for doing this, so stick with the one you're happiest with. If you have no preference then learn the one below.)

The standard format for quadratic equations is:   $ax^2 + bx + c = 0$
Most Exam questions have <u>a = 1</u>, making them <u>much easier</u>.

   E.g.   $x^2 + 3x + 2 = 0$       (See next page for when a is not 1)

## Factorising Method When a = 1

1) <u>ALWAYS</u> rearrange into the <u>STANDARD FORMAT</u>:  $ax^2 + bx + c = 0$

2) Write down the <u>TWO BRACKETS</u> with the x's in:  (x     )(x     )=0

3) Then <u>find 2 numbers</u> that <u>MULTIPLY to give 'c'</u> (the end number) but also <u>ADD/SUBTRACT to give 'b'</u> (the coefficient of x)

4) Put them in and check that the +/− signs work out properly.

## An Example      "Solve  $x^2 - x = 12$  by factorising."

<u>ANSWER</u>:   1)  <u>First rearrange it</u> (into the standard format):  <u>$x^2 - x - 12 = 0$</u>

2)  a = 1, so the initial brackets are (as ever):   <u>(x     )(x     ) = 0</u>

3)  We now want to look at <u>all pairs of numbers</u> that <u>multiply to give c</u> (=12), but which also <u>add or subtract to give the value of b</u>:
   $1 \times 12$  Add/subtract to give:     13 or 11
   $2 \times 6$  Add/subtract to give:      8 or 4      this is what
   $3 \times 4$  Add/subtract to give:      7 or ①  ← we're after (=±b)

4)  So 3 and 4 will give b = ±1, so put them in:  <u>(x     3)(x     4)=0</u>

5)  <u>Now fill in the +/− signs</u> so that the 3 and 4 add/subtract to give -1 (=b), Clearly it must be +3 and −4 so we'll have:   <u>(x + 3)(x − 4)=0</u>

6)  <u>As an ESSENTIAL check, EXPAND the brackets</u> out again to make sure they give the original equation:
   $(x + 3)(x - 4) = x^2 + 3x - 4x - 12 = $ <u>$x^2 - x - 12$</u>

   <u>We're not finished yet mind</u>, because  <u>(x + 3)(x − 4) = 0</u> is only the <u>factorised form of the equation</u> — we have yet to give the actual <u>SOLUTIONS</u>.  This is very easy:

7)  <u>THE SOLUTIONS</u> are simply <u>the two numbers in the brackets</u>, but with <u>OPPOSITE +/− SIGNS</u>:  i.e. <u>x = -3 or +4</u>

   Make sure you remember that last step.  <u>It's the difference</u> between <u>SOLVING THE EQUATION</u> and merely <u>factorising it</u>.

# Factorising Quadratics

## When 'a' is not 1    E.g. $3x^2 + 5x + 2 = 0$

The basic method is still the same but it's a lot messier. Chances are, the Exam question will be with a=1, so make sure you can do that type easily. Only then should you try to get to grips with these harder ones.

## An Example    "Solve $3x^2 + 7x = 6$ by factorising."

1) First rearrange it (into the standard format):   $3x^2 + 7x - 6 = 0$

2) Now because a = 3, the two x-terms in the brackets will have to multiply to give $3x^2$
   so the initial brackets will have to be: $(3x\ \ \ )(x\ \ \ ) = 0$

   (i.e. you put in the x-terms first, with coefficients that will multiply to give 'a')

3) We now want to look at all pairs of numbers that multiply with each other to give 'c'
   (=6, ignoring the minus sign for now):   i.e. $1 \times 6$ and $2 \times 3$

4) Now the difficult bit: to find the combination which does this:

   > multiply with the 3x and x terms in the brackets and then
   > add or subtract to give the value of b (=7):

The best way to do this is by trying out all the possibilities in the brackets until you find the combination that works. Don't forget that EACH PAIR of numbers can be tried in TWO different positions:

| | | | |
|---|---|---|---|
| $(3x\ \ \ 1)(x\ \ \ 6)$ | multiplies to give 18x and 1x | which add/subtract to give | 17x or 19x |
| $(3x\ \ \ 6)(x\ \ \ 1)$ | multiplies to give 3x and 6x | which add/subtract to give | 9x or 3x |
| $(3x\ \ \ 3)(x\ \ \ 2)$ | multiplies to give 6x and 3x | which add/subtract to give | 9x or 3x |
| $(3x\ \ \ 2)(x\ \ \ 3)$ | multiplies to give 9x and 2x | which add/subtract to give | 11x or ⑦x |

   So $(3x\ \ \ 2)(x\ \ \ 3)$ is the combination that gives b = 7, (give or take a +/−)

5) Now fill in the +/− signs so that the combination will add/subtract to give +7 (=b).
   Clearly it must be +3 and −2 which gives rise to +9x and -2x.
   So the final brackets are:   $(3x - 2)(x + 3)$

6) As an ESSENTIAL check, EXPAND the brackets out again to make sure they give the original equation:
   $(3x - 2)(x + 3) = 3x^2 + 9x - 2x - 6 = 3x^2 + 7x - 6$

   > 7) The last step is to get THE SOLUTIONS TO THE EQUATION: $(3x - 2)(x + 3) = 0$
   > which you do by separately putting each bracket = 0 :
   >    i.e. $(3x - 2) = 0 \Rightarrow x = 2/3$   $(x + 3) = 0 \Rightarrow x = -3$
   > Don't forget that last step. Again, it's the difference between
   > SOLVING THE EQUATION and merely factorising it.

## It's not scary — just think of it as brackets giving algebra a hug...

Actually, don't 'cause that won't really help you in the exam. What will help is learning the 7 steps for solving quadratics by factorising — both for 'a = 1' and 'a ≠ 1'. And then answering these questions:
1) Solve these by the factorising method:
a) $x^2 + 5x - 24 = 0$   b) $x^2 - 6x + 9 = 16$   c) $(x + 3)^2 - 3 = 13$   d) $5x^2 - 17x - 12 = 0$

# Sequences

There are different types of <u>number sequence</u> you could get in the exam, each as pretty as the last.
They're not difficult — <u>AS LONG AS YOU WRITE DOWN WHAT'S HAPPENING IN EACH GAP</u>.

## 'State the rule for extending the pattern'

This is what a lot of <u>Exam questions</u> end up asking for and it's easy enough so long as you remember this:

> ALWAYS say what you do to the <u>PREVIOUS TERM</u> to get the next term.

**Example:** 'Add or Subtract a Changing Number'

E.g.  8  11  15  20  26  ...        or        53  43  34  26  19  ...
         +3  +4  +5  +6  +7                        -10  -9  -8  -7  -6

> **The RULE:** 'Add 1 <u>extra</u> each time to the <u>previous term</u>'        'Subtract 1 <u>less</u> from the <u>previous term</u>'

**Example:** 'Multiply by the Same Number each Time'

E.g.   5  10  20  40  ...                        2  6  18  54  ...
          ×2  ×2  ×2  ×2                            ×3  ×3  ×3  ×3

> **The RULE:** 'Multiply the <u>previous term</u> by 2'        'Multiply the <u>previous term</u> by 3'

## Common Difference Type: 'dn + (a – d)'

"<u>The nth term</u>" is a formula with "n" in it which gives you <u>every term in a sequence</u> when you put different values for n in.

For any sequence such as 3, 7, 11, 15, where there is a <u>COMMON DIFFERENCE</u>:

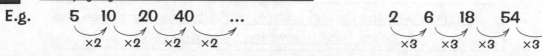

you can always find 'the nth term' using the formula: **'nth term = dn + (a – d)'**

> 1) 'a' is simply the value of <u>THE FIRST TERM</u> in the sequence.
> 2) 'd' is simply the value of <u>THE COMMON DIFFERENCE</u> between the terms.
> 3) To get the <u>nth term</u>, you just find the values of '<u>a</u>' and '<u>d</u>' from the sequence and <u>stick them in the formula</u>. You don't replace n though — that wants to stay as n.
> 4) Of course <u>YOU HAVE TO LEARN THE FORMULA</u>, but life is like that.

**Example:** "Find the nth term of this sequence:   5,  8,  11,  14 ...."
1) The formula is dn + (a – d)
2) The <u>first term</u> is 5, so <u>a = 5</u>. The <u>common difference</u> is 3 so <u>d = 3</u>.
3) Putting these in the formula gives: 3n + (5 – 3) so the <u>nth term = 3n + 2</u>.

## Look, if I've told you n times, I've told you n + 1 times — learn this page...

LEARN the formula for finding the nth number and Bob's your uncle.

1) Find the next two numbers in each of these sequences, and say <u>in words</u> what the rule is for extending each one:
a) 2, 5, 9, 14 ....    b) 2, 20, 200 ....    c) 64, 32, 16, 8 ...
2) Find the expression for the nth number in this sequence:  7,  9,  11,  13

# Z Coordinates and Line Segments

When you get down to it, finding the midpoint is just a spot of <u>adding</u> and <u>dividing by two</u>.

## Z Coordinates are for 3-D space

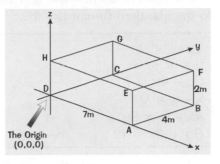

1) All z-coordinates do is extend the normal x-y coordinates into a third direction, z, so that <u>all positions</u> then have <u>3 coordinates</u>:   (x,y,z)

2) This means you can give the coordinates of the <u>corners of a box</u> or any other <u>3-D SHAPE</u>.

For example, in this drawing the coordinates of B and F are B(7, 4, 0)   F(7, 4, 2).

## The 'Midpoint' is just the Middle of the Line

The '<u>MIDPOINT OF A LINE SEGMENT</u>' is the <u>POINT THAT'S BANG IN THE MIDDLE</u> of it.
(Not exactly rocket science, is it...)

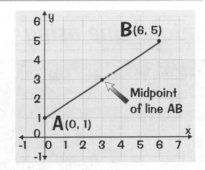

## Find the Coordinates of a Midpoint

The only thing you really need to know about midpoints is how to find the coordinates of one.

And it's pretty easy.  The x-coordinate of the midpoint is the average of the x-coordinates of the end points — and the same goes for the y-coordinates.

**EXAMPLE:**   "A and B have coordinates (2,1) and (6,3)
Find the midpoint of the line AB."

<u>ALWAYS START BY DRAWING A GRAPH</u>

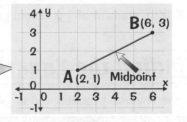

Then follow these <u>THREE EASY STEPS</u>...

1) Find the <u>average</u> of the <u>x-coordinates</u> of the two points.

2) Find the <u>average</u> of the <u>y-coordinates</u> of the two points.

3) Plonk them in <u>brackets</u>.

Average of x-coordinates
= (2 + 6) ÷ 2 = <u>4</u>

Average of y-coordinates
= (1 + 3) ÷ 2 = <u>2</u>

Plonk them in brackets
(x-coordinate first): (<u>4</u>,<u>2</u>)

## To find the midpoint — average, average, plonk

<u>Learn the 3 easy steps</u> for finding midpoints.  Close the book and <u>write them down</u>.
Plot these points on some graph paper: A(1,4), B(5,6), C(3,2), D(7,0).
1) Draw a line between points A and B and find the midpoint of the line AB.
2) Draw a line between points C and D and find the midpoint of line CD.

# $y = mx + c$

Using '$y = mx + c$' is perhaps the 'proper' way of dealing with straight-line equations, and it's a nice trick if you can do it. The first thing you have to do though is <u>rearrange</u> the equation into the standard format like this:

| <u>Straight line:</u> | | <u>Rearranged into '$y = mx + c$'</u> | |
|---|---|---|---|
| $y = 2 + 3x$ | $\rightarrow$ | $y = 3x + 2$ | (m=3, c=2) |
| $2y - 4x = 7$ | $\rightarrow$ | $y = 2x + 3\frac{1}{2}$ | (m=2, c=3½) |
| $x - y = 0$ | $\rightarrow$ | $y = x + 0$ | (m=1, c=0) |
| $4x - 3 = 5y$ | $\rightarrow$ | $y = 0.8x - 0.6$ | (m=0.8, c=-0.6) |
| $3y + 3x = 12$ | $\rightarrow$ | $y = -x + 4$ | (m=-1, c=4) |

<u>REMEMBER:</u>     '<u>m</u>' equals the <u>gradient</u> of the line.
               '<u>c</u>' is the '<u>y-intercept</u>' (where the graph hits the y-axis).

<u>BUT WATCH OUT:</u> people mix up 'm' and 'c' when they get something like $y = 5 + 2x$.
Remember, 'm' is the number <u>in front of the 'x'</u> and 'c' is the number <u>on its own</u>.

## 1) Sketching a Straight Line using $y = mx + c$

1) Get the equation into the form '$\underline{y = mx + c}$'.
2) <u>Put a dot on the y-axis</u> at the value of c.
3) Then go <u>along one unit</u> and <u>up or down by the value of m</u> and make another dot.
4) <u>Repeat</u> the same 'step' in <u>both directions</u>.
5) Finally check that the gradient <u>looks right</u>.

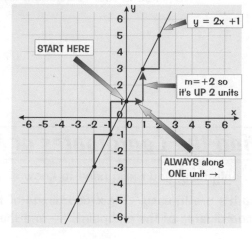

The graph shows the process for the equation '$y = 2x + 1$':

1) '$c$' = 1, so put a first dot at y = 1 on the y-axis.
2) Go along 1 unit $\rightarrow$ and then up by 2 because '$m$' = +2.
3) Repeat the same step, $1 \rightarrow 2\uparrow$ in both directions.
4) CHECK: a gradient of $\underline{+2}$ should be <u>quite steep</u> and <u>uphill</u> left to right which it is, so it looks OK.

## 2) Finding the Equation Of a Straight Line Graph

This is the reverse process and is <u>EASIER</u>.

1) From the axes, <u>identify the two variables</u> (e.g. 'x and y' or 'h and t').
2) <u>Find the values</u> of '<u>m</u>' (gradient) and '<u>c</u>' (y-intercept) from the graph.
3) Using these values from the graph, <u>write down the equation</u> with the standard format '$y = mx + c$'.

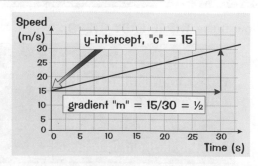

For the example above: '$\underline{S = \frac{1}{2}t + 15}$'

## Remember $y = mx + c$ — it'll keep you on the straight and narrow...

That, and remembering the <u>8 rules</u> for <u>drawing the lines</u> and <u>finding the equations</u>. And eating your greens.

1) Now, sketch these graphs: a) $y = 2 + x$   b) $y = x + 6$   c) $4x - 2y = 0$   d) $y = 1 - \frac{1}{2}x$
   e) $x = 2y + 4$     f) $2x - 6y - 8 = 0$     g) $0.4x - 0.2y = 0.5$     h) $y = 3 - x + 2$

# More Graphs

Ah, what could be better than a nice D/T graph to finish the first half of the Unit with?
OK, so a picture of Keira Knightly might be better. Or Hugh Jackman. But this isn't
called 'Hollywood Hotties' is it...

## Distance-Time Graphs

You need to be able to <u>DRAW</u> and <u>INTERPRET</u>
distance-time graphs for your exam.

Just remember these 3 important points:

1) At any point, <u>GRADIENT = SPEED</u>,
   but watch out for the UNITS.
2) The <u>STEEPER</u> the graph, the <u>FASTER</u> it's going.
3) <u>FLAT SECTIONS</u> are where it is <u>STOPPED</u>.

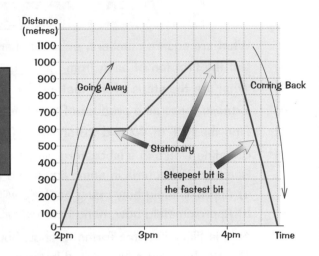

**EXAMPLE:** "What is the speed of the return
section on the graph shown?"

<u>ANSWER:</u> Speed = gradient = 1000 m ÷ 30 mins = **33.33** <u>m/min</u>.

But m/min are naff units, so it's better to do it like this: 1 km ÷ 0.5 hrs = <u>2 km/h</u>

## Parallel and Perpendicular Lines

1) The equation of a straight line is <u>y = mx + c</u> (see previous page)
   where <u>m</u> is the <u>gradient</u> and c is the y-intercept.

2) Parallel lines have the <u>same value of m</u>, i.e. the <u>same gradient</u>.
   So the lines: $y = 2x + 3$, $y = 2x$ and $y = 2x - 4$ are all parallel.

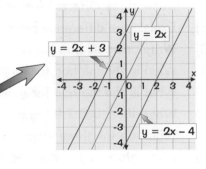

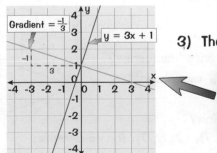

3) The gradients of two <u>perpendicular</u> lines multiply to give <u>–1</u>.

If the gradient of the first line is m, the gradient of
the other line will be $\frac{-1}{m}$, because $m \times \frac{-1}{m} = -1$.

## Moan, moan, moan is all my slope ever does — he's just so negative...

It might not be the most exciting stuff, but it can be worth loads of marks in the exam. Kerching.
Make sure you understand what the different gradients on a D/T graph mean. Then give this a go...

1) For the D/T graph shown above, work out the speed of the middle section in km/h.

# Revision Summary for Unit 2 — Part 1

Aren't graphs great. I think everyone likes graphs.

Anyway, here are the scary questions to find out what you know. By the way, I hope you haven't started trying to kid yourself that these aren't proper maths questions so you don't have to bother with them. Oh no.

Maths is <u>packed</u> with <u>facts</u> — and you need to know them <u>to be able to do it</u>.

All these questions do is see how many of the simple facts you've learnt so far.

Try it now and scare yourself. Then learn some stuff and try again.

## KEEP LEARNING THESE BASIC FACTS UNTIL YOU KNOW THEM

1) What are square numbers, cube numbers and prime numbers?

2) List the first ten of each <u>from memory</u>. Write down the first 5 powers of 2 and the first 5 powers of 10.

3) What are the steps of the method for determining if a number is prime?

4) Express these as a product of prime factors: a) 210 b) 1050

5) Find the <u>HCF</u> of 42 and 28 and the <u>LCM</u> of 8 and 10.

6)* Christine works in a laboratory with a type of bacteria that double in number every 20 minutes.
   She has $2^{10}$ bacteria in some liquid in a test tube. She splits the liquid equally into 2 new test tubes.
   a) Approximately how many bacteria will there be in each test tube now?
   b) Approximately how many bacteria will there be in each test tube after 1 hour?

7)* Anja is filling in some forms to show how much beer has been made at her brewery.
   The numbers must be entered in standard index form. Write Anja's numbers in standard form:
   a) 970 000 cans    b) 6 830 000 bottles   c) 3 560 000 000 pints

8)* Paul needs to set his machine to cut metal sheeting to a thickness of $2.75 \times 10^{-6}$ m.
   The machine won't accept standard index form. What number should Paul type in?

9) Demonstrate the 2 methods for converting recurring decimals to fractions.

10) Describe in words the methods for doing fractions by hand.

11) Name three different forms that a rational number can take, and give examples.

12) Explain the difference between rational and irrational numbers.

13) Write down all you know about manipulating surds.

14) What is the method for multiplying out brackets such as $3(2x + 4)$?

15) What is the method for multiplying pairs of brackets? What about squared brackets?

16) What does 'D.O.T.S.' stand for? Give two examples of it.

17) What are the three steps for factorising expressions such as $12x^2y^3z + 15x^3yz^2$?

18) Give details of the three techniques for doing algebraic fractions, with examples.
   What check should you do to make sure you've done it right?

19) What difference does it make when factorising a quadratic if 'a' is not 1?

20) What is the formula for finding the nth term of a "common difference" sequence?

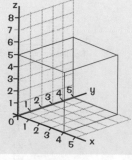

21)* An architect has made a 3D sketch for the design of an extension.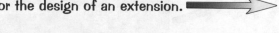
   He has used the scale 2 m to 1 unit.
   a)   What length and width should the builders make the extension?
   b)   Draw the roof onto the sketch using the coordinates (2, 0, 7), (2, 5, 7), for its corners.

22) What does '$y = mx + c$' have to do with? What do 'm' and 'c' represent?

23) List the five steps necessary to draw the graph of '$5x = 2 + y$' using '$y = mx + c$'.

24) List the three steps for obtaining the equation from a straight line graph.

25) Give three important details relating to distance-time graphs.

26) How are the gradients of perpendicular and parallel lines related?

---

# Geometry

If you know _all_ these rules _thoroughly_, you at least have a fighting chance of working out problems with lines and angles. If you don't — you've no chance. Sorry to break it to you like that.

## 7 Simple Rules — that's all:

### 1) Angles in a triangle

...ADD UP TO 180°.

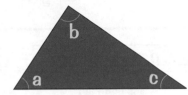

$$a+b+c=180°$$

### 2) Angles on a straight line

...ADD UP TO 180°.

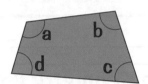

$$a+b+c=180°$$

### 3) Angles in a 4-sided shape   (a 'Quadrilateral')

...ADD UP TO 360°.

You can see why this is if you think of a quadrilateral as two triangles stuck together. Each triangle has angles adding up to 180°, so the two together have angles adding up to 180° + 180° = 360°.

$$a+b+c+d=360°$$

### 4) Angles round a point

...ADD UP TO 360°.

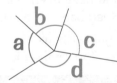

$$a+b+c+d=360°$$

### 5) Exterior Angle of Triangle

EXTERIOR ANGLE of triangle
= SUM OF OPPOSITE INTERIOR ANGLES

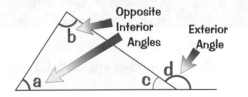

$$a+b=d$$

### 6) Isosceles triangles

2 sides the same
2 angles the same

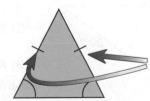

These dashes indicate two sides the same length

In an isosceles triangle, you only need to know _one angle_ to be able to find the other two, which is very useful if you remember it.

a)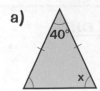

180° − 40° = 140°
The two bottom angles are both the same and they must add up to 140°, so each one must be half of 140°. So x = 70°.

b)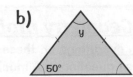

The two bottom angles must be the same, so 50° + 50° = 100°. All the angles add up to 180° so y = 180° − 100° = 80°.

# Geometry

## 7) Parallel Lines

Whenever one line crosses two <u>parallel lines</u> then the two bunches of angles <u>are the same</u>, and <u>a + b = 180°</u>.

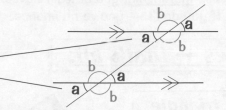

These are called '<u>vertically opposite angles</u>'.

---

You need to spot the <u>characteristic Z, C, U and F shapes</u>:

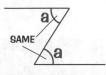 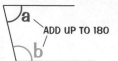  

In a <u>Z-shape</u> they're called '<u>ALTERNATE ANGLES</u>'

If they add up to 180 they're called '<u>SUPPLEMENTARY ANGLES</u>'

In an F-shape they're called '<u>CORRESPONDING ANGLES</u>'

Alas you're expected to learn these three silly names too!

If necessary, <u>EXTEND THE LINES</u> to make the diagram <u>easier to get to grips with</u>:

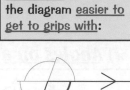

---

# The Basic Approach to Geometry Problems

1) <u>Don't</u> concentrate too much on the angle you have been asked to find. The best method is to find <u>ALL</u> the angles in <u>whatever order</u> they become obvious.

2) <u>Don't</u> sit there waiting for inspiration to hit you. It's all too easy to find yourself staring at a geometry problem and <u>getting nowhere</u>. The method is this:

> <u>GO THROUGH ALL THE ABOVE RULES OF GEOMETRY, ONE BY ONE</u>, and apply each of them in turn <u>in as many ways as possible</u> — one of them is bound to work.

## Example

"Find all the other angles in this diagram."

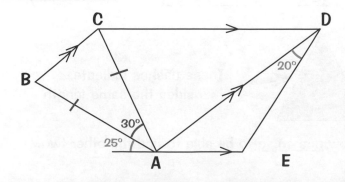

ANSWER:
1) ABC is isosceles, so ∠ABC = ∠ACB = 75°
2) BC and AD are parallel, BCAD is a Z-shape, so if ∠ACB = 75° then ∠CAD = 75° too.
3) Angles on a straight line means ∠EAD = 50°
4) AE and CD are parallel so ∠ADC = 50° also.
5) Triangle ACD adds up to 180° so ∠ACD = 55°
6) Triangle ADE adds up to 180° so ∠AED = 110°

---

## The basic approach to Geometry problems — panic and freak out...

Well, you could. Or you could <u>learn everything</u> on these 2 pages, especially all the stuff on parallel lines, then have a go at these questions. A much better course of action methinks.

1) If one angle of an isosceles triangle is 68°, what values could the other angles have?

2) Find angle x in this diagram and then fill in all the other angles.

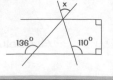

# Polygons

A <u>polygon</u> is a <u>many-sided shape</u>. A <u>regular</u> polygon is one where all the <u>sides</u> and <u>angles</u> are the same. The regular polygons are a never-ending series of shapes with some fancy features. They're very easy to learn. Here are the first few but they don't stop — you can have one with 12 sides or 25, etc.

### EQUILATERAL TRIANGLE
<u>3 sides</u>
<u>3 lines</u> of symmetry
Rot<sup>nl</sup> symm. <u>order 3</u>

### SQUARE
<u>4 sides</u>
<u>4 lines</u> of symmetry
Rot<sup>nl</sup> symm. <u>order 4</u>

### REGULAR PENTAGON
<u>5 sides</u>
<u>5 lines</u> of symmetry
Rot<sup>nl</sup> symm. <u>order 5</u>

### REGULAR HEXAGON
<u>6 sides</u>
<u>6 lines</u> of symmetry
Rot<sup>nl</sup> symm. <u>order 6</u>

### REGULAR HEPTAGON
<u>7 sides</u>
<u>7 lines</u> of symmetry
Rot<sup>nl</sup> symm. <u>order 7</u>
(A 50p piece is like a heptagon)

### REGULAR OCTAGON
<u>8 sides</u>
<u>8 lines</u> of symmetry
Rot<sup>nl</sup> symm. <u>order 8</u>

You also need to know the <u>next two</u>, but I'm not drawing them for you. <u>Learn their names</u>:

## Interior and Exterior Angles

1) Exterior Angles
2) Interior Angles
3) This angle is always the same as the Exterior Angles.
4) Each sector triangle is <u>ISOSCELES</u> (see p.57).

There are 4 formulas to learn:

$$\text{EXTERIOR ANGLE} = \frac{360°}{n}$$

$$\text{INTERIOR ANGLE} = 180° - \text{EXTERIOR ANGLE}$$

$$\text{SUM OF EXTERIOR ANGLES} = 360°$$

$$\text{SUM OF INTERIOR ANGLES} = (n - 2) \times 180°$$

(n is the number of sides)

Note — the two SUM formulas above work for <u>any</u> polygons, not just regular ones.

### REGULAR NONAGON
<u>9 sides</u>, etc. etc.

### REGULAR DECAGON
<u>10 sides</u>, etc. etc.

### REGULAR POLYGONS HAVE LOADS OF SYMMETRY

1) The pentagon shown here has <u>only 3 different angles</u> in the whole diagram.

2) This is <u>typical of regular polygons</u>. They display an amazing amount of symmetry.

3) With a regular polygon, <u>if two angles look the same, they will be</u>. That's not a rule you should normally apply in geometry, and anyway you'll need to <u>prove</u> they're equal.

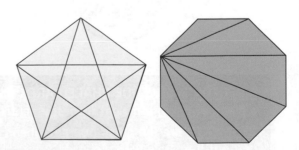

## I'm not going to make the obvious joke. I think we're both above that...

You might think you know a lot of this already, but there's bound to be something new on the page, so <u>learn it all</u>.

1) Work out the two key angles for a regular pentagon. And for a 12-sided regular polygon.

2) A regular polygon has an interior angle of 156°. How many sides does it have?

3) Work out ALL the angles in the pentagon and octagon shown above.

(Aww man, this was gonna be my big break an' everythin'.)

# Symmetry and Circles

Right, there are <u>TWO types</u> of symmetry you need to know about:

## 1) Line Symmetry

This is where you can draw a <u>MIRROR LINE</u> (or more than one) across a picture and both sides will <u>fold exactly</u> together.

 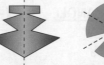  

| H | E | ↓ | ❀ | N | M |
|---|---|---|---|---|---|
| 2 LINES OF SYMMETRY | 1 LINE OF SYMMETRY | 1 LINE OF SYMMETRY | 3 LINES OF SYMMETRY | NO LINES OF SYMMETRY | 1 LINE OF SYMMETRY |

## 2) Rotational Symmetry

This is where you can <u>rotate</u> the shape into different positions that <u>look exactly the same</u>.

If a shape has only 1 position, you can either say 'order 1 symmetry' or 'no rotational symmetry'

| T | Z | S | | |
|---|---|---|---|---|
| Order 1 | Order 2 | Order 2 | Order 3 | Order 4 |

# Tangents, Chords, Arcs and the Rest...

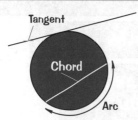

Tangent
Chord
Arc

<u>A TANGENT</u> is a straight line that <u>just touches</u> the <u>outside</u> of the circle.
<u>A CHORD</u> is a line drawn <u>across the inside</u> of a circle.
<u>AN ARC</u> is just <u>part of the circumference</u> of the circle.

### Tangent-Radius Meet at 90°

A tangent always makes an angle of <u>exactly 90°</u> with the <u>radius</u> it meets at this point.

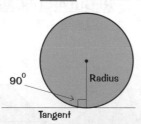

90°
Radius
Tangent

### Equality of Tangents from a Point

The two tangents drawn from an outside point are <u>always equal in length</u>, so creating an 'isosceles' situation, with <u>two congruent right-angled triangles</u>.

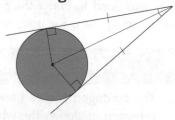

<u>A SECTOR</u> is a WEDGE SHAPED AREA (like a piece of cake) cut right from the centre.
<u>SEGMENTS</u> are the areas you get when you cut the circle with a chord.

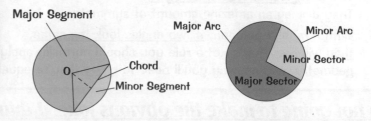

Major Segment
O
Chord
Minor Segment

Major Arc
Minor Arc
Minor Sector
Major Sector

# _I'd like to say I'm a fan of this topic, but I'm not very good at line..._

Get this lot learnt and it'll help you on the way to getting a nice symmetrical A in your exam.  Right then,

1)  Find the lines of symmetry and order of rotational symmetry for:   H   N   E   Y   M   S   T

# Areas and Nets

Yes, I thought I could detect some groaning when you realised that this is a page of formulas that you need to learn.  Well, I'm afraid it's tough — the sooner you get on with it, the <u>sooner</u> you'll have them learnt.

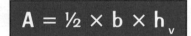

You also need to know <u>area = length × width</u> for a <u>rectangle</u> — but I guess I don't need to remind you of that one.

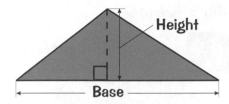

<u>Area of triangle</u> = ½ × base × vertical height

$$A = \tfrac{1}{2} \times b \times h_v$$

Note that the <u>height</u> must always be the <u>vertical height</u>, not the sloping height.

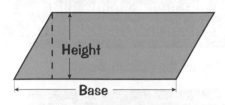

<u>Area of parallelogram</u> = base × vertical height

$$A = b \times h_v$$

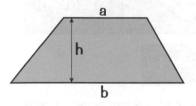

<u>Area of trapezium</u> = average of parallel sides × distance between them

$$A = \tfrac{1}{2} \times (a + b) \times h$$

## Surface Area and Nets

1) <u>SURFACE AREA</u> only applies to solid 3D objects, and it is simply <u>the total area</u> of all the <u>outer surfaces</u> added together.  If you were painting it, it's all the bits you'd paint.

2) <u>A NET</u> is just <u>A SOLID SHAPE FOLDED OUT FLAT</u>.

3) So obviously:

   <u>SURFACE AREA OF SOLID = AREA OF NET</u>.

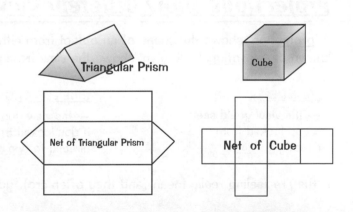

Triangular Prism

Net of Triangular Prism

Cube

Net of Cube

## <u>*I need to take my shape to the barbers — it's getting area and area...*</u>

Hahaha.... Not amused?  OK suit yourself.  It's time to <u>memorise the area formulas</u> and learn how to deal with <u>complicated shapes</u>.  Then find the areas of these 4 shapes...

1)

3 cm

4 cm

2)

4 m

6 m

3)

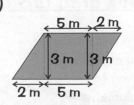

5 m   2 m

3 m   3 m

2 m   5 m

4)

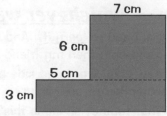

7 cm

6 cm

5 cm

3 cm

# Volume and Projections

You might think you know some of this already, but I bet you don't know it all. There's only one thing for it...

## LEARN these volume formulas...

## 1) Cuboid (rectangular block)

(This is also known as a 'rectangular prism' — see below to understand why.)

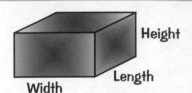

Height

Length

Width

Volume of Cuboid = length × width × height

$$V = L \times W \times H$$

(The other word for volume is CAPACITY.)

## 2) Prism

**A PRISM** is a solid (3-D) object which is the same shape all the way through — i.e. it has a **CONSTANT AREA OF CROSS-SECTION**.

For some reason, not a lot of people know what a prism is, but they come up all the time in Exams, so make sure **YOU** know.

### Triangular Prism

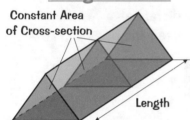

Constant Area of Cross-section

Length

| VOLUME OF PRISM | = | CROSS-SECTIONAL AREA | × LENGTH |
|---|---|---|---|

$$V = A \times L$$

As you can see, the formula for the volume of a prism is _very simple_. The _difficult_ part, usually, is _finding the area of the cross-section_.

## Projections Show Different Viewpoints

A '_projection_' shows the shape of an object from either the _front_, _side_ or _back_ — they're usually known as '_elevations_'. A '_plan_' shows the view from _above_. Projections and plans are always _drawn to scale_.

**FRONT ELEVATION**
— the view you'd see if you looked from directly in _front_:

**SIDE ELEVATION**
— the view you'd see if you looked from directly to _one side_:

**PLAN**
— the view you'd see if you looked from directly _above_:

If they're feeling really mean (and they often are), you might get a question on:

**ISOMETRIC PROJECTION** — this is where the shape is drawn (again, to scale) from a view at _equal angles to_ all three axes (_x, y_ and _z_). Or more simply, it's a drawing like this:

This one's a bit trickier, so you might want to spend a little longer practising it — just to get your head round it.

## Yep — whichever way you look at it, this is a pretty dull page...

But you need to _learn it_. And learn it good.

Then, and only then my friend do you get to answer these:

1) Draw plan, front and side elevations and an isometric projection of your house.

2) What type of shape is this? Find its volume.

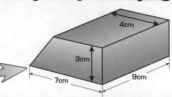

4cm

3cm

7cm

9cm

# Metric and Imperial Units

A nice easy page for a change — just some <u>facts</u> to learn.  Hooray!

## Metric Units

1) <u>Length</u>   mm, cm, m, km
2) <u>Area</u>   $mm^2$, $cm^2$, $m^2$, $km^2$,
3) <u>Volume</u>   $mm^3$, $cm^3$, $m^3$, ml, litres
4) <u>Weight</u>   g, kg, tonnes
5) <u>Speed</u>   km/h,  m/s

| MEMORISE THESE KEY FACTS: | |
| --- | --- |
| 1 cm = 10 mm | 1 tonne = 1000 kg |
| 1 m  = 100 cm | 1 litre  = 1000 ml |
| 1 km = 1000 m | 1 litre = 1000 $cm^3$ |
| 1 kg  = 1000 g | 1 $cm^3$ = 1 ml |

## Metric-Imperial Conversions

<u>YOU NEED TO LEARN THESE</u>  — they don't promise to give you these in
the Exam and if they're feeling mean (as they often are), they won't.

### APPROXIMATE CONVERSIONS

| | |
| --- | --- |
| 1 kg ≈ 2.2 lbs | 1 gallon ≈ 4.5 litres |
| 1 litre ≈ 1¾ pints | 1 foot ≈ 30 cm |
| 1 inch ≈ 2.5 cm | 1 mile ≈ 1.6 km  (or  5 miles ≈ 8 km) |

### Using Metric-Imperial Conversion Factors

1) Convert 37 inches into cm.   CF = 2.5, so × and ÷ by 2.5, to get 14.8 cm or <u>92.5 cm</u>.
2) Convert 5.45 litres into pints.  CF = 1¾, so × and ÷ by 1.75, to get 3.11 or <u>9.54 pints</u>.

## You'll be Given Any Other Conversion Factors

**EXAMPLE:**

"If £1 = 1.7 US Dollars, how much is 63 US dollars in £s?"

1) Obviously, conversion factor = <u>1.7</u> (The "exchange rate")
2) 63 × 1.7 = £107.10
   63 ÷ 1.7 = £37.06
3) Not quite so obvious this time, but since 1.7 US dollars = £1, you're
   clearly going to have <u>less</u> pounds than you had dollars (roughly half).
   So the answer has to be <u>less than</u> 63, which means it must be <u>£37.06</u>

## Watch out — give some people an inch and they'll take 2.5 cm...

Learn the <u>conversion factors</u> in the shaded boxes above.  Then <u>turn over and write them down</u>.  Hmm, I don't
know about you, but I quite fancy some conversion based questions after all that.  Which is convenient...

1)  How many litres is 3 gallons?
2)  A calculator is 6 inches long.  What is this in cm?
3)  Petrol costs £4.50 per gallon.  What does it cost per litre?
4)  A car travels at 50 mph.  What is its speed in km/h?

# Speed, Distance and Time

Speed-distance-time questions are <u>very common</u>, and they never give you the formula!
Either you learn it beforehand or you wave goodbye to several easy marks.

## 1) The Formula Triangle

Of course you have to <u>remember the order of the letters</u> in the triangle (SDT),
and this time we have the word <u>SoDiT</u> to help you. So if it's a question on
speed, distance and time just say: <u>SOD IT</u>.

<u>EXAMPLE</u>: "A car travels 90 miles at 36 miles per hour. How long does it take?"
<u>ANS</u>:  We want to find the <u>time</u>, so <u>cover up T</u> in the triangle which leaves D/S,
      so T = D/S   = distance ÷ speed  = 90 ÷ 36 = <u>2.5 hours</u>

> IF YOU <u>LEARN THE FORMULA TRIANGLE</u>, YOU WILL FIND
> QUESTIONS ON SPEED, DISTANCE AND TIME <u>VERY EASY</u>.

## 2) Units — Getting them Right

<u>Units</u> should always be in your mind when you <u>write an answer down</u>. When you're using a **FORMULA**, there is
one special thing you need to know. It's simple enough, but you must know it:

> The <u>UNITS you get out</u> of a Formula
> <u>DEPEND ENTIRELY</u> upon <u>the UNITS you put into it</u>.

For example, if you put a <u>distance in cm</u> and a <u>time in seconds</u> into the formula triangle to work
out **SPEED**, the answer must come out in <u>cm per second</u> (cm/s).

If the <u>time is in hours</u> and the speed in <u>miles per hour</u> (mph) then the distance you calculate will
come out in <u>miles</u>.   It's pretty simple when you think about it.

### But Don't Mix Units

E.g.  Don't mix <u>Miles Per HOUR</u> in a formula with a <u>time in MINUTES</u>  (convert it to <u>hours</u>).
     Don't mix <u>DENSITY IN g/cm³</u> in a formula with a <u>MASS IN kg</u>  (convert it to g).

**Example:** "A boy walks 800m in 10 minutes. Find his speed in km/h."
If you use 800m and 10 minutes your answer will be a speed in <u>metres per minute</u> (m/min).
Instead you must <u>convert</u>:  800m = <u>0.8 km</u>,   10 mins = <u>0.1667 hours</u> (mins÷60).
Then you can divide 0.8 km by 0.1667 hours to get <u>4.8 km/h</u>.

## <u>Together we shall rule the universe as finger and formula triangle...</u>

Oh yes, it is your <u>destiny</u>. One step at a time though. First of all you need to learn this page, so turn over and
briefly summarise both topics, with examples. Keep trying until you can <u>remember it all</u>. Then as your big finale:
1)  Find the time taken, in hours and minutes, for a purple-nosed buffalo walking at 4.2 km/h to cover 6.3 km.
2)  Also find how far it would go in 45 mins. Give your answer in both km and m.

# Revision Summary for Unit 2 — Part 2

More difficult questions, <u>but just keep reminding yourself that they're the very best revision you can do</u>. These questions don't ask anything too tricky, just whether or not you've actually <u>learnt</u> all the <u>basic facts</u> in Unit 2.  It's really important to keep practising these as often as you can.

## KEEP LEARNING THESE BASIC FACTS UNTIL YOU KNOW THEM

1) Write down the seven easy rules of geometry.

2) What are vertically opposite angles?

3) What are regular polygons?  Name the first eight.

4) List the special features that regular polygons have.

5) What do you know about their symmetry?

6) Draw a circle and show what an arc, a sector, a segment and a chord are.

7) There are three formulas for area you should know straight off.  Write them all down.

8)* Clive is re-carpeting his lounge, which is rectangular.  The room is 12 m long and 7 m wide. The carpet he wants costs £5 per m². How much will it cost Clive to carpet his lounge?

9) What is meant by a net?  How is it related to surface area?

10) Sketch the nets for these shapes:
a) triangular prism   b) cube    c) cuboid    d) square-based pyramid.

11) What is a prism?  Sketch three different ones.

12) There are two formulas for volume you should know.
Write them them down.

13)* A juice company makes apple squash in batches of 9000 cm³.  The squash is sold in cartons that have a constant cross-sectional area of 50 cm² and a height of 6 cm. How many of these cartons can the company fill from one batch of apple squash?

14)* An architect has drawn up plans for an extension to a house, shown below.

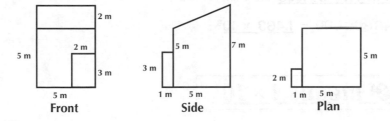

Front          Side          Plan

Make a 3D sketch of the extension.

15) Give 8 metric conversions and 6 metric-to-imperial.

16)* Kylie is on holiday in South Africa, where £1 = 11 rand.  She pays 220 rand to go to a safari park. How much has she spent in pounds?

17) What is the formula triangle for speed, distance and time?

18) What two main rules apply to the units involved with formula triangles?

* Answers to these questions are on p108.

# Calculating with Standard Index Form

## Three Very Important Examples

## 1) The Calculator's Scientific Mode

1)   This mode <u>gives all numbers in standard form</u> to a specified number of sig fig.

2)   A little SCI will be displayed somewhere when you're in this mode.

3)   To get into this mode, press MODE and select SCI from one of the menus you get.
     (On other calculators look for a button with 'SCI' written above it as the 2nd or 3rd function.)

It'll ask you for the number of sig figs to display, something like this:  `SCI  0-9?`

So if you choose 4, all numbers and answers will be displayed to 4 sig fig.

> <u>EXAMPLE:</u>   565 ÷ 3 would give  `188.3333333`  in normal mode,
>
> ...or  `1.883⁰²`  in 4 sig fig mode.

## 2) What is 146.3 Million in Standard Form?

The two favourite <u>wrong answers</u> for this are:

1)   $146.3 \times 10^6$ — which is kind of right but it's not in <u>STANDARD FORM</u>
     because 146.3 is not between 1 and 10 (i.e. $1 \leq A < 10$ has not been done)

2)   $1.463 \times 10^6$ — this one <u>is</u> in standard form but it's not big enough.

This is a very typical Exam question, which <u>too many people get wrong</u>.
Just <u>take your time</u> and <u>do it IN TWO STAGES</u> like this:

<u>ANSWER:</u> 146.3 million = 146 300 000 = <u>$1.463 \times 10^8$</u>

## 3) Remember, $10^5$ means $1 \times 10^5$

So to enter $10^5$ into the calculator you must remember it's actually $1 \times 10^5$ and press  [1] [EXP] [5]

> <u>EXAMPLE:</u>   "A nanometre is $10^{-9}$ m.  How many nanometres are there in 0.35 m?"
>
> ANSWER:   $0.35 \div (1 \times 10^{-9})$, so press [0.35] [÷] [1] [EXP] [(-)] [9] [=] = $3.5 \times 10^8$.

## This stuff's a lot more fun than I were EXPectin'...

Learn the <u>three important examples</u>, then turn over and <u>write them down</u>.  Then lookie here...

1)   Express 0.854 million and 0.00018 in standard index form.

2)   Express $4.56 \times 10^{-3}$ and $2.7 \times 10^5$ as ordinary numbers.

3)   a) Work out  $3.2 \times 10^7 \div 1.6 \times 10^{-4}$.
     b) How many nanometres are there in $10^{-1}$ m?

# Proportion and Variation

## Direct Proportion: $y = kx$

**BOTH INCREASE TOGETHER**

## Inverse Proportion: $y = k/x$

One **INCREASES** , one **DECREASES**

1) The graph of y against x is a <u>straight line through the origin</u>: $y = kx$

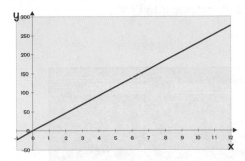

1) The graph of y against x is the well known $y = k/x$ graph:

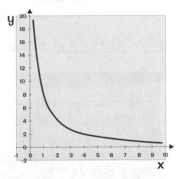

2) In a table of values the **MULTIPLIER** is the <u>same for x and y</u>, i.e. if you <u>double</u> one of them, you <u>double</u> the other, if you <u>times one of them by 3</u>, you <u>times the other by 3</u>, etc.

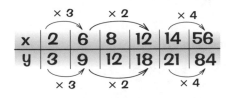

2) In a table of values the **MULTIPLIER** for one of them becomes a **DIVIDER** for the other, i.e. if you <u>double one</u>, you <u>half the other</u>, if you <u>treble one</u>, you <u>divide the other by three</u>, etc.

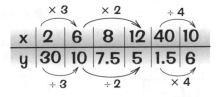

3) The <u>**RATIO**</u> $\dfrac{x}{y}$ is the same for all pairs of values, i.e from the table above:

$$\frac{2}{3} = \frac{6}{9} = \frac{8}{12} = \frac{12}{18} = \frac{14}{21} = \frac{56}{84} = 0.6667$$

3) The <u>**PRODUCT**</u> xy (x times y) is the <u>same</u> for <u>all pairs of values</u>, i.e. in the table above:

$$2 \times 30 = 6 \times 10 = 8 \times 7.5 = 12 \times 5$$
$$= 40 \times 1.5 = 10 \times 6 = \underline{60}$$

## Inverse Square Variation

You can have all sorts of relationships between x and y, like $y = kx^2$ or $y = k/x^3$ etc. as detailed on the next page. The most important type is $\underline{y = k/x^2}$ and is called '<u>INVERSE SQUARE</u>' variation. <u>DON'T MIX UP THIS NAME</u> with <u>inverse proportion</u>, which is just $y = k/x$.

## <u>*A bear, ate a square, in underwear (that's a square in verse, actually...)*</u>

Learn the <u>3 key features</u> for both <u>direct</u> and <u>inverse</u> proportion. Then <u>turn over</u> and <u>write them all down</u>.
1) Give examples of 2 real quantities that exhibit: a) direct- and b) inverse proportion.
2) Make up your own tables of values which show: a) direct proportion   b) inverse proportion

# Proportion and Variation

This page shows you how to deal with questions which involve statements like these:
    'y is proportional to the square of x'        't is proportional to the square root of h'
    'D varies with the cube of t'                'V is inversely proportional to r cubed'
To deal successfully with things like this <u>you must remember this method</u>:

## Method:

1) <u>Convert the sentence into a proportionality</u>,
                using the symbol '$\propto$' which means '<u>is proportional to</u>'.

2) <u>Replace '$\propto$' with '$=k$'</u> to make an <u>EQUATION</u>:

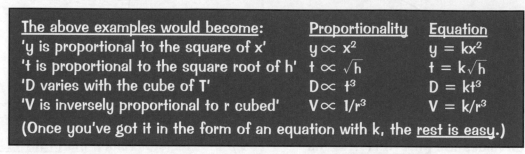

| The above examples would become: | Proportionality | Equation |
|---|---|---|
| 'y is proportional to the square of x' | $y \propto x^2$ | $y = kx^2$ |
| 't is proportional to the square root of h' | $t \propto \sqrt{h}$ | $t = k\sqrt{h}$ |
| 'D varies with the cube of T' | $D \propto t^3$ | $D = kt^3$ |
| 'V is inversely proportional to r cubed' | $V \propto 1/r^3$ | $V = k/r^3$ |

(Once you've got it in the form of an equation with k, the <u>rest is easy</u>.)

3) <u>Find a PAIR OF VALUES of x and y</u> somewhere in the question,
                and <u>SUBSTITUTE them into the equation</u> with the <u>sole purpose of finding k</u>.

4) <u>Put the value of k back into the equation</u>
                and it's now ready to use, e.g. $y = 3x^2$.

5) <u>INEVITABLY, they'll ask you to find y</u>,
                having given you a value for x (or vice versa).

## Example:

The time taken for a duck to fall down a chimney (it happens!) is inversely proportional to the square of the diameter of the flue. If she took 25 seconds to descend a chimney of diameter 0.3 m, how long would it take her to get down one of 0.2 m diameter?

(Notice there's no mention of 'writing an equation' or 'finding k'
— it's up to <u>YOU</u> to remember the method for yourself.)

<u>ANSWER</u>:

1)  Write it as a <u>proportionality</u>, then an <u>equation</u>:      $t \propto 1/d^2$   i.e.   $t = k/d^2$
2)  <u>Sub in the given values</u> for the two variables:      $25 = k/0.3^2$
3)  Rearrange the equation to <u>find k</u>:      $k = 25 \times 0.3^2 = 2.25$
4)  Put k <u>back in</u> the formula:      $t = 2.25/d^2$
5)  <u>Sub in new value</u> for d:      $t = 2.25/0.2^2 = \underline{56.25\ secs}$

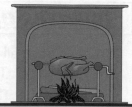

## Joy $\propto$ 1/algebra...

This is all pretty straightforward. As long as you learn the <u>five steps of the method</u> plus the <u>four examples</u>. Then <u>turn over and write them all down</u>. Then do this question. Then make me a lovely cup of tea. ☺

1)  The frequency of a pendulum is inversely proportional to the square root of its length. If the pendulum swings with a frequency of 0.5 Hz when the length is 80 cm, what frequency will it have with a length of 50 cm, and what length will give a frequency of 0.7 Hz?

# Percentage and Proportion Change

You did a load of stuff on percentage calculations and percentage change back in Unit 1. You'll need all that for this Unit too, but you need a few extra bits as well.

## Calculate the Original Amount from the Percentage Change

THESE QUESTIONS ARE IDENTIFIED BY <u>NOT</u> GIVING THE "<u>ORIGINAL VALUE</u>"

These are the type of percentage question that most people get wrong – but only because they don't recognise them and don't apply this simple method:

**EXAMPLE:**

> A house increases in value by 20% to £72,000. Find what it was worth <u>before</u> the rise.

**METHOD:**

$$\div 120 \begin{cases} £72,000 = 120\% \\ £600 = 1\% \end{cases}$$
$$\times 100 \begin{cases} £600 = 1\% \\ £60,000 = 100\% \end{cases}$$

So the original price was <u>£60,000</u>

An <u>INCREASE</u> of 20% means that £72,000 represents <u>120% of the original</u> value. If it was a <u>DROP</u> of 20%, then we would put '£72,000 = <u>80%</u>' instead, and then divide by 80 on the LHS, instead of 120.

Always set them out <u>exactly like this example</u>. The trickiest bit is deciding the top % figure on the RHS — the 2nd and 3rd rows are <u>always</u> 1% and 100%.

## Repeated Proportional Change Problems

**EXAMPLE:**

> "Ali buys a really big potato for £800. Her potato loses one quarter of its value each year. Find the value of Ali's potato after 3 years."

Value after 1 year is: £800 × 0.75 = £600

Value after 2 years is: £600 × 0.75 = £450

Value after 3 years is: £450 × 0.75 = £337.50

A loss of ¼ is the same as a loss of 25%. So you need to work out 100 − 25 = 75% of the original value. 75% as a decimal is 0.75.

So you're basically just multiplying by 0.75 for <u>each year</u>.

A quicker way of <u>setting this out</u> would be:
£800 × 0.75 × 0.75 × 0.75, or even better: <u>£800 × 0.75³</u>.

If you had to work out the potato's value in say, 58 years, you'd <u>have</u> to do it this way. This is like the compound interest calculations you did in Unit 1 (see p.6).

## Reality TV show error #52 — it's impossible to give 110%......

Make sure you know the methods for these <u>two types</u> of percentage problem inside-out. And don't forget all the stuff you learnt in Unit 1 either. Those sneaky examiners could ask you about <u>ANY</u> of it.

1) A car depreciates by 30% to £14,350. What was it worth before?

2) Find the value after 4 years of an emu that cost £30 and loses 10% value per year.

# Bounds and Reciprocals

At first, it might seem like these two topics are pretty unrelated. That's because <u>they are</u>. Don't let that bother you though, they've <u>both</u> still got to be learned.

## 1) <u>Upper and Lower Bounds of a Measurement</u>

The simple rule is this:

> The real value can be as much as **HALF THE ROUNDED UNIT** above and below the rounded-off value.

E.g. If a length is given as 2.4 m to the nearest 0.1 m, the rounded unit is 0.1 m so the real value could be anything up to 2.4 m ÷ 0.05 m giving answers of 2.45 m and 2.35 m for the upper and lower bounds.

## 2) <u>Maximum and Minimum Values for Calculations</u>

When a calculation is done using rounded-off values there will be a <u>DISCREPANCY</u> between the <u>CALCULATED VALUE</u> and the <u>ACTUAL VALUE</u>:

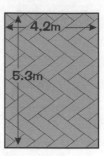

<u>EXAMPLE:</u> A floor is measured as being 5.3 m × 4.2 m to the nearest 10 cm.
This gives an area of <u>22.26 m$^2$</u>, but this is not the actual floor area because
the real values could be anything from <u>5.25 m to 5.35 m</u> and <u>4.15 m to 4.25 m</u>,
∴ Maximum possible floor area = 5.35 × 4.25 = <u>22.7375 m$^2$</u>,
∴ Minimum possible floor area = 5.25 × 4.15 = <u>21.7875 m$^2$</u>.

## <u>Reciprocals — Learn these 4 Facts</u>

1) The reciprocal of a number is '<u>one over</u>' the number. 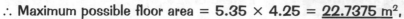 The reciprocal of $5 = \dfrac{1}{5}$.

2) You can find the reciprocal of a fraction by turning it <u>upside down</u>. The reciprocal of $\dfrac{3}{8} = \dfrac{8}{3}$.

3) A number <u>multiplied by its reciprocal</u> gives <u>1</u>. $\dfrac{6}{7} \times \dfrac{7}{6} = 1$

4) 0 has no reciprocal because <u>you can't divide anything by 0</u>.

## The $\boxed{^1/_x}$ (or $\boxed{x^{-1}}$) Button Makes Reciprocals much Easier

This has two very useful functions:

1) <u>Making divisions a bit slicker</u>. E.g. if you already have 2.3456326 in the display and you want to do 12 ÷ 2.3456326, then you can just press $\boxed{÷}$ $\boxed{12}$ $\boxed{=}$ $\boxed{^1/_x}$ $\boxed{=}$, which does the division <u>the wrong way up</u> and then <u>flips it the right way up</u>.

2) <u>Analysing decimals</u> to see if they might be rational,
e.g. if the display is 0.142857142 and you press $\boxed{^1/_x}$ $\boxed{=}$ you'll get 7, meaning it was $\dfrac{1}{7}$ before.

## <u>Never trust reciprocals — they're always trying to get one over on you...</u>

Learn all the <u>bits and bobs</u> on this page then <u>turn over</u> and see how much you can remember. Try this too:

1) x and y are measured as 2.32 m and 0.45 m to the nearest 0.01 m.
   a) Find the upper and lower bounds of x and y.
   b) If z = x + 1/y, find the max and min possible values of z.

Careful here — the biggest input values don't always give the biggest result.

# Solving Equations

Solving equations means finding the value of x from something like: $3x + 5 = 4 - 5x$.
Now, not a lot of people know this, but exactly the same method applies to both solving equations and rearranging formulas (see p.77).

> 1) EXACTLY THE SAME METHOD APPLIES TO BOTH FORMULAS AND EQUATIONS.
> 2) THE SAME SEQUENCE OF STEPS APPLIES EVERY TIME.

To illustrate the sequence of steps we'll use this equation: $\sqrt{2 - \dfrac{x+4}{2x+5}} = 3$

## The Six Steps Applied to Equations

1) Get rid of any square root signs by squaring both sides:   $2 - \dfrac{x+4}{2x+5} = 9$

2) Get everything off the bottom by cross-multiplying up to EVERY OTHER TERM:

$$2 - \frac{x+4}{2x+5} = 9 \quad \Rightarrow \quad 2(2x+5) - (x+4) = 9(2x+5)$$

3) Multiply out any brackets:   $4x + 10 - x - 4 = 18x + 45$

4) Collect all subject terms on one side of the '=' and all non-subject terms on the other. Remember to reverse the +/– sign of any term that crosses the '='

+18x moves across the '=' and becomes –18x
+10 moves across the '=' and becomes –10
–4 moves across the '=' and becomes +4

$4x + 10 - x - 4 = 18x + 45$

$4x - x - 18x = 45 - 10 + 4$

5) Combine together like terms on each side of the equation, and reduce it to the form 'Ax = B', where A and B are just numbers (or bunches of letters, in the case of formulas):

-15x = 39
('Ax = B':
A = -15, B = 39, x is the subject)

6) Finally slide the A underneath the B to give '$x = \dfrac{B}{A}$', divide, and that's your answer.

$x = \dfrac{39}{-15} = -2.6$
So $\underline{x = -2.6}$

## The Seventh Step (if You Need It)

If the term you're trying to find is squared, don't panic.

Follow steps 1) to 6) like normal, but solve it for $x^2$ instead of x:

$x^2 = 9$
$x = \pm 3$

7) Take the square root of both sides and stick a ± sign in front of the expression on the right:

Don't forget the ± sign...
(P.43 if you don't know what I mean).

## Solving equations — more fun than greasing a seal...

Definitely. I never ever exaggerate. Learn the 7 steps for solving equations. Then have a go at answering these:

1) Solve these equations: a) $5(x + 2) = 8 + 4(5 - x)$   b) $\dfrac{4}{x+3} = \dfrac{6}{4-x}$   c) $x^2 - 21 = 3(5 - x^2)$

# Simultaneous Equations and Graphs

When you have <u>two graphs</u> which represent <u>two separate equations</u>, there are two ways the question can present it: <u>two simultaneous equations</u> or a <u>single merged equation</u>. In either case the solutions will simply be <u>where the two graphs cross</u>...

## 1) Two Graphs and Two Separate Equations

**Example 1:**

"Draw the graphs for "$y = 2x + 3$" and "$y = 6 - 4x$" and then use your graphs to solve the equations."

Just draw the graphs and read off the x- and y- values where they cross...

$$\underline{x = \tfrac{1}{2} \text{ and } y = 4}$$

Where they cross
$\underline{x = \tfrac{1}{2}, y = 4}$

**Example 2:**

"By drawing graphs, solve the simultaneous equations $x^2 + y^2 = 16$ and $y = 2x + 1$."

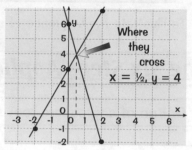

1) <u>DRAW BOTH GRAPHS</u>.

$x^2 + y^2 = 16$ is the equation of a circle, centre (0, 0), radius 4 (see p.83)

2) <u>LOOK FOR WHERE THE GRAPHS CROSS</u>.

The straight line crosses the circle at <u>two points</u>. Reading the <u>x and y values</u> of these points gives the solutions $x = 1.4$, $y = 3.8$ and $x = -2.2$, $y = -3.4$ (to 1 decimal place).

## 2) Two Graphs but Just ONE Equation, or so it seems...

**Example**

"Using the graphs shown for $y = 4 + \tfrac{1}{2}x$ and $y = 6 - x^2/3$, <u>solve the equation</u>: $x^2/3 + \tfrac{1}{2}x - 2 = 0$."

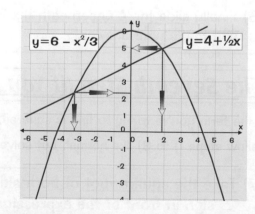

1) <u>ANSWER</u>: <u>Learn</u> these important steps:
   <u>Equating the equations</u> of the two graphs gives this:
   $6 - x^2/3 = 4 + \tfrac{1}{2}x$ (a sort of '<u>merged</u> equation')

2) Now bring it all onto <u>one side</u> and you end up with:
   $x^2/3 + \tfrac{1}{2}x - 2 = 0$ (the equation in the question!)

3) Hence the <u>solutions</u> to that equation are where the two initial equations ($y = 4 + \tfrac{1}{2}x$ and $y = 6 - x^2/3$) are <u>equal</u> — i.e. where their <u>graphs cross</u>, which as the graph shows is at: <u>$x = 1.8$</u> or <u>$x = -3.3$</u>.

## What do you call a giraffe with no eyes? A graph...

...well, a graffe. Doesn't work so well on paper, does it. Ho hum... learn the page and try these questions.
1) Use graphs to find the solutions to these pairs of equations:
   a) $y = 4x - 4$ and $y = 6 - x$     b) $y = 2x$ and $y = 6 - 2x$
2) Draw the graphs of $y = 2x^2 - 4$ and $y = 2 - x$ and hence solve $2x^2 + x = 6$.

*Unit 3 — Number, Algebra and Geometry 2*

# Simultaneous Equations

You've seen the easy way to solve simultaneous equations using graphs. Now it's time to learn the less fun algebra methods. The rules are really quite simple, but <u>you must follow ALL the steps, in the right order, and treat them as a strict method</u>.

There are two types of simultaneous equations you could get
— **EASY ONES** (where both equations are linear) and **TRICKY ONES** (where one's quadratic).

①  $2x = 6 - 4y$  and  $-3 - 3y = 4x$          ②  $7x + y = 1$  and  $2x^2 - y = 3$

## ① Six Steps For EASY Simultaneous Equations

We'll use these two equations for our example:  $2x = 6 - 4y$  and  $-3 - 3y = 4x$

1) <u>Rearrange both equations</u> into the form <u>$ax + by = c$</u> where a, b, c are numbers, (which can be negative). Also label the two equations  —① and  —②

$$2x + 4y = 6 \quad — ①$$
$$-4x - 3y = 3 \quad — ②$$

2) You need to <u>match up the numbers in front</u> (the 'coefficients') of either the x's or y's in both equations. To do this you may need to multiply one or both equations by a suitable number. You should then relabel them:  —③ and  —④

$$① \times 2 : \quad 4x + 8y = 12 \quad — ③$$
$$-4x - 3y = 3 \quad — ④$$

3) <u>Add or subtract the two equations</u> to eliminate the terms with the same coefficient
If the <u>coefficients are the same</u> (both +ve or both –ve) then <u>SUBTRACT</u>
If the <u>coefficients are opposite</u> (one +ve and one –ve) then <u>ADD</u>

$$③ + ④ \quad 0x + 5y = 15$$

4) Solve the resulting equation to find whichever letter is left in it.

$$5y = 15 \Rightarrow \underline{y = 3}$$

5) Substitute this value back into equation ① and solve it to find the other quantity.

Sub in ① :  $2x + 4 \times 3 = 6 \Rightarrow 2x + 12 = 6 \Rightarrow 2x = -6 \Rightarrow \underline{x = -3}$

6) Then substitute both these values into equation ② to make sure it works.
If it doesn't then you've done something wrong and you'll have to do it all again.

Sub x and y in ② :  $-4 \times -3 - 3 \times 3 = 12 - 9 = \underline{3}$,  which is right, so it's worked.
So the solutions are:  $\underline{x = -3}$,  $\underline{y = 3}$

## Sunday morning, lemon squeezy and simultaneous linear equations...

...all easy apparently. Easy or not, you need to learn the <u>6 steps</u> on this page. Remember, you only know them when you can write them all out from memory, so turn over the page and see if you can write down all six.
1)  Apply the six steps to find F and G given that  $2F - 10 = 4G$  and  $3G = 4F - 15$

# Simultaneous Equations

## ② Seven Steps For TRICKY Simultaneous Equations

Example:  Solve these two equations simultaneously:  $7x + y = 1$  and  $2x^2 - y = 3$

**1)** **Rearrange the quadratic equation** so that you have the **non-quadratic unknown on its own**.  Label the equations ① and ② .

$$7x + y = 1 \quad —①$$
$$y = 2x^2 - 3 \quad —②$$

**2)** **Substitute the quadratic expression** into the **other equation**. You'll get another equation — label it ③ .

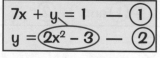

$$7x + (2x^2 - 3) = 1 \quad —③$$

In this example you just shove the expression for y into equation ① , in place of y.

**3)** **Rearrange** to get a **quadratic equation**. And guess what...  You've got to **solve it**.

$$2x^2 + 7x - 4 = 0$$

That factorises into:          Check this step by multiplying out again:
$$(2x - 1)(x + 4) = 0 \qquad (2x - 1)(x + 4) = 2x^2 - x + 8x - 4 = 2x^2 + 7x - 4 \ ☺$$
So, $2x - 1 = 0$  OR  $x + 4 = 0$
In other words, $\underline{x = 0.5}$  OR  $\underline{x = -4}$

If it won't factorise, you can either use the <u>quadratic formula</u> or <u>complete the square</u>.  Have a look at P.75-76 for more details.

**4)** Stick the **first value back in** one of the **original equations** (pick the easy one).

① $7x + y = 1$   Substitute in $x = 0.5$: $3.5 + y = 1$, so $\underline{y = 1 - 3.5 = -2.5}$

**5)** Stick the **second value back in** the same **original equation** (the easy one again).

① $7x + y = 1$   Substitute in $x = -4$: $-28 + y = 1$, so $\underline{y = 1 + 28 = 29}$

**6)** **Substitute** both pairs of answers back into the other **original equation** to **check** they work.

② $y = 2x^2 - 3$

Substitute in $x = 0.5$ and $y = -2.5$: $-2.5 = (2 \times 0.25) - 3 = -2.5$ — jolly good.
Substitute in $x = -4$ and $y = 29$:    $29 = (2 \times 16) - 3 = 29$ — smashing.

**7)** **Write the pairs of answers out again**, **CLEARLY**, at the bottom of your working.

The two pairs of answers are:    $\underline{x = 0.5 \text{ and } y = -2.5}$ or $\underline{x = -4 \text{ and } y = 29}$

(Do this even if you think it's <u>pointless and stupid</u>.  If there's even the <u>remotest chance</u> of the examiner getting the pairs mixed up, it's worth a <u>tiny bit of extra effort</u>, don't you think.)

## Simultaneous pain and pleasure — it must be algebra...

...there's just no substitute for it.  Except maybe love.  Anyway learn the <u>7 steps</u>, then solve these for f and g:

a)  $f = g^2 + 4$  and  $f - 6g - 4 = 0$          b)  $13g - f = -7$  and  $3g^2 - f = 3$
c)  $4g + f = 3$  and  $f = 4g^2$               d)  $g = 4f^2 - 3$  and  $g + 11f = 0$

# The Quadratic Formula

In Unit 2, you found out how to solve quadratic equations by factorising. Well there are two more methods you need for Unit 3. The solutions to any quadratic equation $ax^2 + bx + c = 0$ are given by this formula:

$$x = \frac{-b \pm \sqrt{b^2 - 4ac}}{2a}$$

<u>LEARN THIS FORMULA</u> — If you can't learn it, there's no way you'll be able to use it in the Exam, even if they give it to you. Using it should, in principle, be quite straightforward. As it turns out though there are quite a few pitfalls, so <u>TAKE HEED of these crucial details</u>:

## Using The Quadratic Formula

1) Always write it down in stages as you go. Take it nice and slowly — any fool can rush it and get it wrong, but there's no marks for being a clot.

2) <u>MINUS SIGNS</u>. Throughout the whole of algebra, minus signs cause untold misery <u>because people keep forgetting them</u>. In this formula, there are two minus signs that people keep forgetting: <u>the -b and the -4ac</u>.

The -4ac causes particular problems <u>when either 'a' or 'c' is negative</u>, because it makes the -4ac effectively +4ac — <u>so learn to spot it as a HAZARD before it happens</u>.

> WHENEVER YOU GET A MINUS SIGN, <u>THE ALARM BELLS SHOULD ALWAYS RING!</u>

3) Remember you <u>divide ALL of the top line by 2a</u>, not just half of it.

4) Don't forget it's <u>2a</u> on the bottom line, not just a. This is another common mistake.

## Example:

"Find the solutions of $3x^2 + 7x = 1$ to 2 decimal places."

The mention of decimal places in Exam questions is a <u>very big clue</u> to use the formula rather than trying to factorise it!

## Method:

1) First get it into the form <u>$ax^2 + bx + c = 0$</u>:  $3x^2 + 7x - 1 = 0$

2) Then carefully identify a, b and c:  <u>$a = 3$,  $b = 7$,  $c = -1$</u>

3) Put these values into the quadratic formula and <u>write down each stage</u>:

$$x = \frac{-b \pm \sqrt{b^2 - 4ac}}{2a} = \frac{-7 \pm \sqrt{7^2 - 4 \times 3 \times -1}}{2 \times 3} = \frac{-7 \pm \sqrt{49 + 12}}{6}$$

$$= \frac{-7 \pm \sqrt{61}}{6} = \frac{-7 \pm 7.81}{6} = 0.1350 \text{ or } -2.468$$

So to 2 DP, the solutions are: <u>$x = 0.14$ or $-2.47$</u>

4) Finally, <u>as a check</u> put these values back into the <u>original equation</u>:
E.g. for $x = 0.1350$:  $3 \times 0.135^2 + 7 \times 0.135 = 0.999675$, which is 1, as near as...

## Enough number crunches? Now it's time to work on your quads...

Learn the <u>4 crucial details</u> and the <u>4 steps of the method</u> for using the Quadratic Formula, then turn over and write them all down. Done it? Now it's time to practice your mad new skillz with these handy questions...

1) Find the solutions of these equations (to 2 DP) using the Quadratic formula:
a) $x^2 + 10x - 4 = 0$    b) $3x^2 - 3x = 2$    c) $(2x + 3)^2 = 15$

# Completing the Square

$$x^2 + 12x - 5 = (x + 6)^2 - 41$$

The SQUARE...                    ...COMPLETED

## Solving Quadratics by 'Completing The Square'

This is quite a clever way of solving quadratics, but it's perhaps a bit confusing at first.
The name 'Completing the Square' doesn't help — it's called that because you basically:

> 1) Write down a <u>SQUARED</u> bracket, and then
> 2) Stick a number on the end to '<u>COMPLETE</u>' it.

It's quite easy if you learn all the steps — some of them aren't all that obvious.

## Method:

1) As always, <u>REARRANGE THE QUADRATIC INTO THE STANDARD FORMAT:</u>
$$ax^2 + bx + c = 0$$

2) <u>If 'a' is not 1 then divide the whole equation by 'a' to make sure it is!</u>

3) Now <u>WRITE OUT THE INITIAL BRACKET:</u>  $(x + b/2)^2$

   NB: <u>THE NUMBER IN THE BRACKET</u> is always <u>HALF THE (NEW) VALUE OF 'b'</u>

4) <u>MULTIPLY OUT THE BRACKETS</u> and <u>COMPARE TO THE ORIGINAL</u>
   to find what extra is needed, and add or subtract the adjusting amount.

## Example:

"<u>Express  $x^2 - 6x - 7 = 0$  as a completed square, and hence solve it.</u>"

The equation is already in the standard form and 'a' = 1, so:

1) The coefficient of x is -6, so the squared brackets must be:  $(x - 3)^2$

2) <u>Square out the brackets:</u>  $x^2 - 6x + 9$, <u>and compare</u> to the original:  $x^2 - 6x - 7$.
   To make it like the original equation it needs -16 on the end, hence we get:

   $$(x - 3)^2 - 16 = 0  \text{ as the alternative version of }  x^2 - 6x - 7 = 0$$

Don't forget though, we wish to <u>SOLVE</u> this equation, which entails these 3 special steps:

1) <u>Take the 16 over</u> to get:          $(x - 3)^2 = 16$.
2) Then <u>SQUARE ROOT BOTH SIDES</u>:     $(x - 3) = \pm 4$  <u>AND DON'T FORGET THE</u> $\pm$
3) <u>Take the 3 over</u> to get:          $x = \pm 4 + 3$   <u>so x = 7 or -1</u>  (don't forget the $\pm$)

## ...but, if a square's not complete, is it really a square...?

Deep.  Go over this carefully, 'cos it's pretty gosh darn confusing at first.  Learn the <u>4 steps</u> for
completing the square and the <u>3 special steps</u> for <u>solving the equation</u>.  Then flex your brain with these...

1)  Find the solutions of these equations (to 2 DP) by completing the square:
   a)  $x^2 + 10x - 4 = 0$    b) $3x^2 - 3x = 2$       c) $(2x + 3)^2 = 15$

# <u>Rearranging Formulas</u>

<u>Rearranging formulas</u> means making one letter the subject, e.g. getting 'y= ' from '2x + z = 3(y + 2p).'
Generally speaking 'solving equations' is easier, but don't forget:

> 1) **EXACTLY THE SAME METHOD APPLIES TO BOTH FORMULAS AND EQUATIONS**
> 2) **THE SAME SEQUENCE OF STEPS APPLIES EVERY TIME.**

We'll illustrate this by making 'y' the subject of this formula: $\quad M = \sqrt{2K - \dfrac{K^2}{2y + 1}}$

## <u>The Six Steps Applied to Formulas</u>

1) **Get rid of any square root signs by <u>squaring both sides</u>:** $\quad M^2 = 2K - \dfrac{K^2}{2y + 1}$

2) **Get everything off the bottom by <u>cross-multiplying</u> up to <u>EVERY OTHER TERM</u>:**

$$M^2 = 2K - \frac{K^2}{2y + 1} \Rightarrow M^2(2y + 1) = 2K(2y + 1) - K^2$$

3) **<u>Multiply out</u> any brackets:** $\qquad 2yM^2 + M^2 = 4Ky + 2K - K^2$

4) **Collect all <u>subject terms</u> on one side of the '=' and all <u>non-subject terms</u> on the other. Remember to reverse the +/− sign of any term that crosses the '='.**

+4Ky moves across the '=' and becomes −4Ky $\qquad 2yM^2 + M^2 = 4Ky + 2K - K^2$
+M² moves across the '=' and becomes −M² $\qquad 2yM^2 - 4Ky = -M^2 + 2K - K^2$

5) **<u>Combine together like terms</u> on each side of the equation, and reduce it to the form '<u>Ax = B</u>', where A and B are just bunches of letters which <u>DON'T</u> include the subject (y). Note that the LHS has to be <u>FACTORISED</u>:**

$$(2M^2 - 4K)y = 2K - K^2 - M^2$$

('Ax = B' i.e. A = (2M² − 4K), B = 2K − K² − M², y is the subject)

6) **Finally <u>slide the A underneath the B</u> to give 'x = $\dfrac{B}{A}$', (cancel if possible) and that's your answer.** $\qquad$ So $y = \dfrac{2K - K^2 - M^2}{(2M^2 - 4K)}$

## <u>The Seventh Step (if You Need It)</u>

$$M = \sqrt{2K - \frac{K^2}{2y^2 + 1}}$$

If the term you're trying to make the subject of the equation is squared, this is what you do:

Follow steps 1) to 6), and then... $\qquad y^2 = \dfrac{2K - K^2 - M^2}{(2M^2 - 4K)}$ $\qquad$ (I've skipped steps 1) - 6) because they're exactly the same as the first example — but with y² instead of y.)

7) **<u>Take the square root</u> of both sides and stick a ± sign in front of the expression on the right:** $\qquad y = \pm\sqrt{\dfrac{2K - K^2 - M^2}{(2M^2 - 4K)}}$ $\qquad$ Remember — square roots can be +ve or −ve. See P.43.

## <u>*If I could rearrange my subjects, I'd have maths all day every day...*</u>

But that's probably just me. Learn the <u>7 steps</u> for <u>rearranging formulas</u>. Then get rearrangin' with these:
1) Rearrange 'F $= \frac{9}{5}$C + 32' from 'F= ', to 'C= ' and then back the other way.
2) Make p the subject of these: a) $\dfrac{p}{p + y} = 4$ $\quad$ b) $\dfrac{1}{p} = \dfrac{1}{q} + \dfrac{1}{r}$ $\quad$ c) $\dfrac{1}{p^2} = \dfrac{1}{q} + \dfrac{1}{r}$

# Inequalities

Inequalities aren't <u>half as difficult as they look</u>. Once you've learned the tricks involved, most of the algebra for them is <u>identical to ordinary equations</u>.

## The Inequality Symbols:

> means '<u>Greater than</u>'    ≥ means '<u>Greater than or equal to</u>'
< means '<u>Less than</u>'    ≤ means '<u>Less than or equal to</u>'

<u>REMEMBER</u>, the one at the <u>BIG</u> end is <u>BIGGEST</u>

so  $x > 4$  and  $4 < x$  both say: '<u>x is greater than 4</u>'

## Algebra With Inequalities

The thing to remember here is that <u>inequalities are just like regular equations</u>
in the sense that all the normal rules of algebra apply <u>WITH ONE BIG EXCEPTION</u>:

$5x < x + 2$
$5x = x + 2$

Whenever you MULTIPLY OR DIVIDE BY A <u>NEGATIVE NUMBER</u>,
you must <u>FLIP THE INEQUALITY SIGN</u>.

## Three Important Examples

I > All of you.

**1) Solve  $5x < 6x + 2$**

The equivalent equation is  $5x = 6x + 2$, which is easy — and so is the inequality:

First subtract 6x from both sides:    $5x - 6x < 2$  which gives  $-x < 2$
Then divide both sides by -1:    $x > -2$  (i.e. x is greater than -2)
*(NOTE: The < has flipped around into a >, because we divided by a negative number)*

**2) Find all integer values of x where $-4 \leq x < 1$**

This type of expression is <u>very common</u> — <u>you must learn them in this way</u>:
'x is between -4 and +1, possibly equal to -4 but never equal to +1'.
    (Obviously the answers are <u>-4, -3, -2, -1, 0</u>  (but not 1))

**3) Find the range of values of x where $x^2 \leq 25$**

The trick here is: <u>Don't forget the negative values</u>.

Square-rooting both sides gives $x \leq 5$. However, this is <u>only half the story</u>,

because $-5 \leq x$ is also true.  There is little alternative but to simply learn this:

$x^2 \leq 25$ gives the solution $-5 \leq x \leq 5$,
(x is between -5 and 5, possibly equal to either).
$x^2 \geq 36$ gives the solution $x \leq -6$ or $6 \leq x$
(x is 'less than or equal to -6' or 'greater than or equal to +6').

## I saw you flip the inequality sign — how rude...

Learn all of this page including the <u>three important examples</u>, then turn over and write it all down.  Now try these:
1)  Solve this inequality: $4x + 3 \leq 6x + 7$
2)  Find all integer values of p, such that   a) $p^2 < 49$   b) $-20 < 4p \leq 17$

# Inequalities

You can show inequalities <u>graphically</u>, too.

## You Can Show Inequalities on Number Lines

**EXAMPLE:** "Show the solution to $x^2 \leq 25$ on a number line."

From the previous page, you know the solution to this is $-5 \leq x \leq 5$

You draw it like this:

The <u>filled circles</u> mean the solution <u>includes</u> the numbers 5 and -5. If your inequality had a < or > instead of a ≤ or ≥, you'd draw an <u>open circle</u> (O).

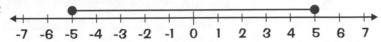

## Solve More Than One Inequality at Once on a Graph

*Awesome things that definitely don't involve any dying.*

**Method**

1) **CONVERT each INEQUALITY to an EQUATION** by simply putting an '=' in place of the '<' or '>'

2) **DRAW THE GRAPH FOR EACH EQUATION**

3) **Work out WHICH SIDE of each line you want** Put x=0 and y=0 into the inequality to see if the <u>ORIGIN</u> is on the correct side.

4) **SHADE THE REGION this gives you**

**Example** "Shade the region represented by: $x + y < 5$, $y > x + 2$ and $y > 1$"

1) <u>**CONVERT EACH INEQUALITY TO AN EQUATION**</u>:
The inequalities become $x + y = 5$, $y = x + 2$ and $y = 1$

2) <u>**DRAW THE GRAPH FOR EACH EQUATION**</u> (see p36)

3) <u>**WORK OUT WHICH SIDE OF EACH LINE YOU WANT**</u>
This is the fiddly bit. Substitute $x = 0$ and $y = 0$ (the origin) into each inequality and see if this makes the inequality <u>true</u> or <u>false</u>.

> <u>In $x + y < 5$</u>: $x = 0$, $y = 0$ gives $0 < 5$ which is <u>true</u>.
> This means the <u>origin</u> is on the <u>correct</u> side of the line.
>
> <u>In $y > x + 2$</u>: $x = 0$, $y = 0$ gives $0 > 2$ which is <u>false</u>.
> So the origin is on the <u>wrong side</u> of this line.
>
> <u>In $y > 1$</u>: $x = 0$, $y = 0$ gives $0 > 1$ which is <u>false</u>.
> So the origin is on the <u>wrong side</u> of this line too.

The <u>dotted lines</u> mean the solution <u>doesn't</u> include the points on the line. If your inequality had a ≤ or ≥ instead of a < or >, you'd draw a <u>solid line</u>.

4) <u>**SHADE THE REGION**</u>
You want the region that satisfies all of these:
– below $x + y = 5$ (because the origin <u>is</u> on this side)
– left of $y = x + 2$ (because the origin <u>isn't</u> on this side)
– above $y = 1$ (because the origin <u>isn't</u> on this side).

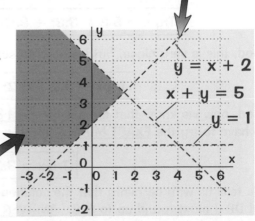

## Graphical inequalities — it's a shady business...

Learn the <u>four steps</u> for doing <u>graphical inequalities</u>, then <u>turn over</u> and <u>write them down</u>. And for even more fun:

1) Show on a graph the region described by the following three conditions:
$x + y \leq 6$, $y \geq 0.5$, $y \leq 2x - 2$

# Trial and Improvement

In principle, this is an easy way to find approximate answers to quite complicated equations. __BUT__... you have to make an effort to __LEARN THE FINER DETAILS__ of this method, otherwise you'll never get the hang of it.

## Method:

1) __SUBSTITUTE TWO INITIAL VALUES__ into the equation that give __OPPOSITE CASES.__ *These are usually suggested in the question. If not, you'll have to think of your own. 'Opposite cases' means one answer too big, one too small. If your values don't give opposite cases try again.*

2) Now __CHOOSE YOUR NEXT VALUE IN BETWEEN__ THE PREVIOUS TWO, and __SUBSTITUTE__ it into the equation. *Continue this process, always choosing a new value between the two closest opposite cases, (and preferably nearer to the one which is closest to the answer you want).*

3) __AFTER ONLY 3 OR 4 STEPS__ you should have __2 numbers__ which are to the __right degree of accuracy but DIFFER BY 1 IN THE LAST DIGIT.__ *For example if you had to get your answer to 2 DP then you'd eventually end up with say 5.43 and 5.44, with these giving OPPOSITE results of course.*

4) __At this point__ you ALWAYS take the __Exact Middle Value__ to decide which is the answer you want. *E.g. for 5.43 and 5.44, you'd try 5.435 to see if the real answer was between 5.43 and 5.435 or between 5.435 and 5.44 (See below).*

## Example:

The equation $x^2 + x = 14$ has a solution between 3 and 3.5. Find this solution to 1 DP.

| Try x = 3 | $3^2 + 3 = 12$ | (Too small) | ← (2 opposite cases) |
| Try x = 3.5 | $3.5^2 + 3.5 = 15.75$ | (Too big) | |

14 is what we want and it's slightly closer to 15.75 than it is to 12 so we'll choose our next value for x a bit closer to 3.5 than 3:

Try x = 3.3   $3.3^2 + 3.3 = 14.19$   (Too big)

Good, this is very close, but we need to see if 3.2 is still too big or too small:

Try x = 3.2   $3.2^2 + 3.2 = 13.44$   (Too small)

Good, now we know that __the answer must be between 3.2 and 3.3__. To find out which one it's nearest to, we have to try the __EXACT MIDDLE VALUE__:  3.25

Try x = 3.25   $3.25^2 + 3.25 = 13.81$   (Too small)

This tells us with certainty that the solution must be between 3.25 (too small) and 3.3 (too big), and so to 1 DP __it must round up to 3.3__. __ANSWER = 3.3__

## Mmmm... jam...

To succeed with this method you must __learn the 4 steps above__. Do it now, and practise until you can write them down __without having to look back at them__. It's not as difficult as you think. Now try this...

1) The equation $x^2 - 2x = 1$ has a solution between 2 and 3. Find it to 1 DP.

# Quadratic Graphs

Quadratic functions can sound pretty darn impressive — "What did you do in maths today, dear?", "Drawing quadratic functions and solving them graphically, mum." Have no fear, with a bit of practice you too can sound this... er... cool, as well as picking up lots of marks in your exams.

## Plotting and Solving Quadratic Functions

Quadratic functions are of the form $y = \underline{\text{anything with } x^2}$ (but not higher powers of x).
Notice that all these $x^2$ graphs have the same <u>SYMMETRICAL</u> bucket shape.

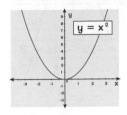
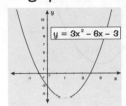
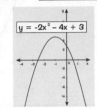

So when you plot a quadratic, remember that you're aiming for a symmetrical bucket shape — anything else is a sure sign that you've gone wrong. Here's how to tackle questions on quadratics.

### 1) Fill in The Table of Values

**Example** "Fill in the table of values for the equation $y = x^2 + 2x - 3$ and draw the graph."

| x | -5 | -4 | -3 | -2 | -1 | 0 | 1 | 2 | 3 |
|---|----|----|----|----|----|---|---|---|---|
| y |    | 5  |    | -3 | -4 | -3 | 0 |   |   |

Work out each point <u>very carefully</u>, writing down all your working. Don't just plug it all straight in your calculator — you'll make mistakes. To check you're <u>doing it right</u>, make sure you can <u>reproduce</u> the y-values they've already given you.

### 2) Draw the Curve

1) <u>PLOT THE POINTS CAREFULLY</u>, and don't mix up the x and y values.

2) The points should form a <u>COMPLETELY SMOOTH CURVE</u>. If they don't, they're <u>wrong</u>.

<u>NEVER EVER</u> let one point drag your line off in some ridiculous direction. When a graph is generated from an equation, you never get spikes or lumps — only <u>MISTAKES</u>.

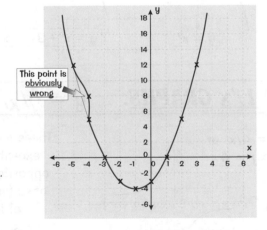

This point is obviously wrong

### 3) Read off the Solutions

**Example** "Use your graph to solve the equation $x^2 + 2x - 3 = 0$."

1) Look — the equation you've been asked to solve is what you get when you put <u>y=0</u> into the graph's equation, $y = x^2 + 2x - 3$.

2) To solve the equation, all you do is read the x-values where y = 0, i.e. where it crosses the x-axis.

3) So the solutions are <u>x = -3</u> and <u>x = 1</u>. (Quadratic eqns usually have 2 solutions.)

4) Celebrate the only way graphs know how: line dancing.

## How refreshing — a page on graphs. Not seen one of those in a while...

You know the deal by now — learn what's on this page, then treat yourself to answering the question below.

1) Plot the graph of $y = x^2 - x - 6$ (use x-values from -4 to 5).
Use your graph to solve the equation $x^2 - x - 6 = 0$.

# Some Harder Graphs to Learn

Graphs come in all sorts of shapes, sizes and wiggles — here are the six types of graph you need to know:

## 1) x² BUCKET SHAPES:    $y = ax^2 + bx + c$    (where b and/or c can be zero)

These graphs all have the same <u>symmetrical bucket shape</u>.

If the x² bit has a '–' in front of it then the bucket is <u>upside down</u>.

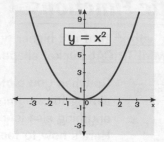
$y = x^2$

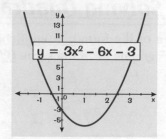
$y = 3x^2 - 6x - 3$

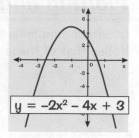
$y = -2x^2 - 4x + 3$

## 2) x³ GRAPHS:    $y = ax^3 + bx^2 + cx + d$    (b, c and/or d can be zero)

All x³ graphs have the <u>same wiggle</u> in the middle — sometimes it's a flat wiggle, sometimes it's more pronounced.

<u>–x³ graphs</u> always go <u>down from top left</u>, <u>+x³</u> ones go <u>up from bottom left</u>.

(Note that x³ must be the highest power and there must be no other bits like 1/x etc.)

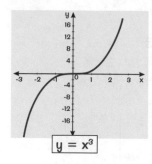
$y = x^3$

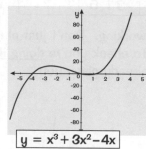
$y = x^3 + 3x^2 - 4x$

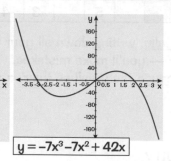
$y = -7x^3 - 7x^2 + 42x$

## 3) 1/x GRAPHS:    $y = {}^A/_x$, or $xy = A$    (A is any number — positive or negative)

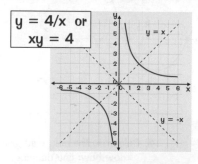
$y = 4/x$ or $xy = 4$

These are <u>all the same basic shape</u>, except the negative ones are in opposite quadrants to the positive ones (as shown). The two halves of the graph don't touch.

They're all <u>symmetrical</u> about the lines $y = x$ and $y = -x$.

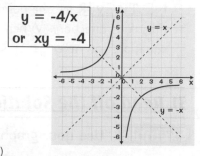
$y = -4/x$ or $xy = -4$

(You get this type of graph with inverse proportion — see P.67)

## 4) kˣ GRAPHS:    $y = k^x$    (k is some positive number)

1) These graphs <u>curve upwards</u> when k > 1.
2) They're always <u>above the x-axis</u>.
3) They all <u>go through the point (0, 1)</u>.
4) For <u>bigger values of k</u>, the graph tails off towards zero <u>more quickly</u> on the left and <u>climbs more steeply</u> on the right.

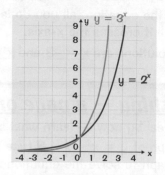

# Some Harder Graphs to Learn

The examiners expect you to know these graphs and be able to sketch them <u>from memory</u>.
They don't ask for much do they...

## 5) CIRCLES: $x^2 + y^2 = r^2$

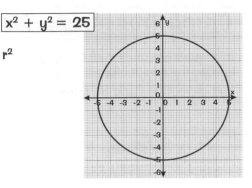

The equation for a circle with <u>centre (0, 0)</u> and <u>radius r</u> is: $x^2 + y^2 = r^2$

$x^2 + y^2 = 25$ is a circle with centre (0, 0).
   $r^2 = 25$, so the radius, r, is 5.
$x^2 + y^2 = 100$ is a circle with centre (0, 0).
   $r^2 = 100$, so the radius, r, is 10.

## 6) TRIG GRAPHS: $y = \sin x$ or $y = \cos x$

### $y = \sin x$

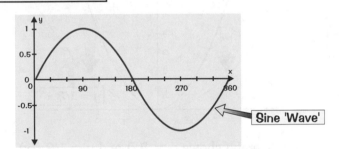

Sine 'Wave'

### $y = \cos x$

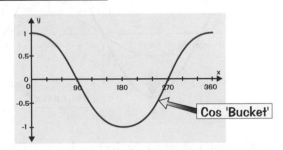

Cos 'Bucket'

1) <u>For 0° – 360°</u>, the shapes you get are a <u>Sine 'Wave'</u> (one peak, one trough) and a <u>Cos 'Bucket'</u> (starts at the top, dips, and finishes at the top).

2) The underlying shape of both the sin and cos graphs are <u>identical</u>, when you extend them (indefinitely) in both directions:

3) The only difference is that the <u>sin graph</u> is shifted right by 90° compared to the cos graph.

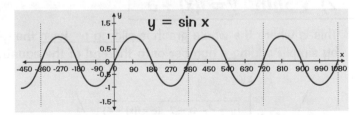

4) Note that both graphs wiggle between <u>y-limits of exactly +1 and -1</u>.

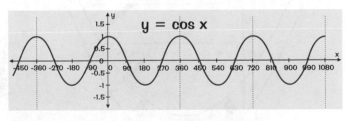

## Phew — these pages could seriously drive you round the $k^x$

Learn the <u>6 types of graph</u>, both their equations and their shapes, then turn over and <u>sketch examples</u> of each.

1) Describe the following graphs <u>in words</u>:
   a) $y = 3x^2 + 2$     b) $y = 4 - x^3$     c) $xy = 2$     d) $x^2 + y^2 = 36$
   e) $x = -7/y$     f) $3x^2 = y - 4x^3 + 2$     g) $y = x - x^2$     h) $y = 5^x$

# Graphs: Shifts and Stretches

Don't be put off by function notation involving f(x). It doesn't mean anything complicated, it's just a fancy way of saying "an equation in x". In other words "y = f(x)" just means "y = some totally mundane equation in x, which we won't tell you, we'll just call it f(x) instead to see how many of you get in a flap about it".

## Graph Transformations

In a question on transforming graphs they will either use function notation or they'll use a known function instead. There are only four different types of graph transformations so just learn them and be done with it. Here they are in order of difficulty:

### 1) y-Stretch: $y = k \times f(x)$

This is where the original graph is stretched along the y-axis by multiplying the whole function by a number, i.e. $y = f(x)$ becomes $y = kf(x)$ (where k = 2 or 5 etc.).
If k is less than 1, then the graph is squashed down in the y-direction instead:

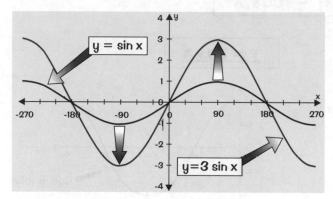
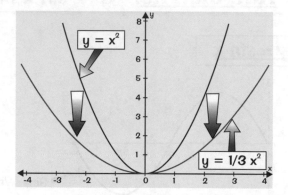

This graph shows $y = f(x)$ and $y = 3f(x)$
($y = \sin x$ and $y = 3 \sin x$)

This graph shows $y = f(x)$ and $y = 1/3 \, f(x)$
($y = x^2$ and $y = 1/3 \, x^2$)

### 2) y-Shift: $y = f(x) + a$

This is where the whole graph is slid up or down the y-axis with no distortion, and is achieved by simply adding a number onto the end of the equation: $y = f(x) + a$.

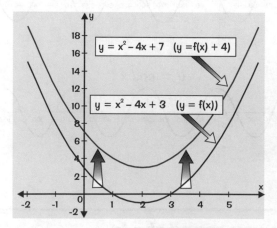
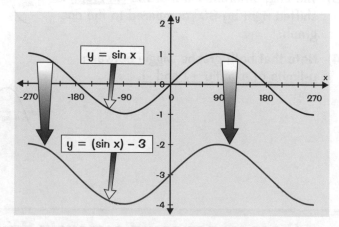

This shows $y = f(x)$ and $y = f(x) + 4$
i.e. $y = x^2 - 4x + 3$, and
$y = (x^2 - 4x + 3) + 4$
or $y = x^2 - 4x + 7$

This shows $y = f(x)$ and $y = f(x) - 3$
i.e $y = \sin x$ and $y = (\sin x) - 3$

# Graphs: Shifts and Stretches

Keep going, there's two more transformations for you to know before you're done with shifts and stretches.

## 3) x-Shift:  y = f(x − a)

This is where the whole graph <u>slides to the left or right</u> and it only happens when you replace '<u>x</u>' everywhere in the equation <u>with 'x − a'</u>.  These are a bit tricky because they go '<u>the wrong way</u>'.  In other words if you want to go from $y = f(x)$ to $y = f(x − a)$ you must move the whole graph a distance 'a' in the <u>positive</u> x-direction → (and vice versa).

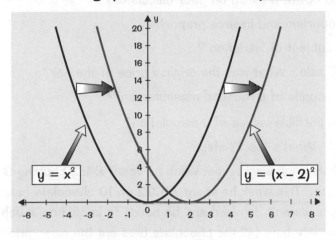

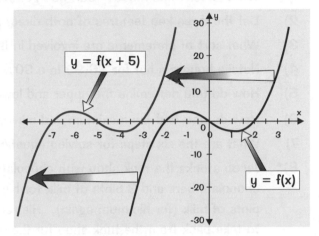

This graph shows <u>y = f(x)</u> and <u>y = f(x − 2)</u>
(i.e. $y = x^2$ and $y = (x − 2)^2$ )

This graph shows <u>y = f(x)</u> and <u>y = f(x + 5)</u>
i.e. $y = x^3 − 4x$, and $y = (x + 5)^3 − 4(x + 5)$

## 4) x-Stretch:  y = f(kx)

These go '<u>the wrong way</u>' too — when k is a '<u>multiplier</u>' it <u>scrunches the graph up</u>, whereas when it's a '<u>divider</u>', it <u>stretches</u> the graph out.  (The opposite of the y-stretch.)

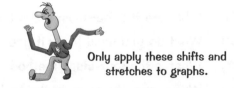

Only apply these shifts and stretches to graphs.

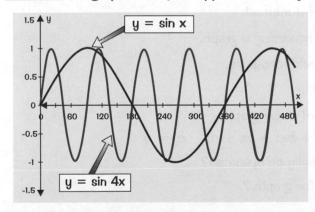

This graph shows <u>y = sin x</u> and <u>y = sin(4x)</u>
The one that is all squashed up is y = sin (4x).
The way to sketch it is simply that with a multiplier of 4, it will be **4 times as squashed up.**

(Each full cycle of up-and-down takes ¼ the amount of x-axis as the original graph, so you fit 4 of them into 1 of the other graph.)

Remember, if k is a <u>divider</u>, then the graph <u>spreads out</u>.  So if the squashed up graph above was the original, <u>y = f(x)</u>, then the more spread out one would be <u>y = f(x/4)</u>.

---

## Shift, stretch... HOLD                                              ...and relax...

Learn the <u>four types of graph transformations</u>, both the effect on the formula and the effect on the graph.
Then <u>turn over</u> and <u>draw two examples of each type</u>.  And a picture of an elephant dressed as a cow.  Good.
Sketch these graphs:      $y = x^2$        $y = x^2 − 4$        $y = 3x^2$        $y = (x − 3)^2$        $y = \cos x$
                                   $y = \cos (x + 30^0)$        $y = \cos x + 3$        $y = 2\cos x − 4$

# Revision Summary for Unit 3 — Part 1

Unit 3's got some pretty nasty stuff in — grisly grimsdike algebra. But grisly or not, you still have to learn it. Don't forget, you've got to keep trying these <u>over and over again</u>. Making sure that you can do these questions is the <u>best revision</u> you can possibly do. Just keep practising till you can glide through them all like a turtle or something.

## KEEP LEARNING THESE BASIC FACTS UNTIL YOU KNOW THEM

1) What is scientific mode? Can you get in and out of it easily on your calculator?

2) List the three key features of both direct proportion and inverse proportion.

3) What sort of statements are involved in the subject of 'variation'?

4)* Natalie bought a hat for £6.99 in a 30% off sale. What was the original price of the hat?

5) How do you determine the upper and lower bounds of a rounded measurement?

6) How do you find the maximum and minimum possible values of a calculation?

7) What are the six steps for solving equations? What's the 7<sup>th</sup> step?

8)* Jacob stocks the tuck shop with chocolate bars each week. Last week he spent £4.20 buying 6 chocolate bars and 3 pints of milk for his mum. This week he spent £5.32 on 10 chocolate bars and 2 pints of milk (for his mum again). His receipts weren't itemised and he needs to know how much money to take back from the tuck shop for the chocolate bars (all the chocolate bars are the same price).
a) Write simultaneous equations for Jacob's two receipts.
b) Solve the equations to calculate how much money Jacob is owed.

9) Write down the formula for solving quadratics.

10) What are the three main pitfalls that catch people out with the quadratic formula?

11) What are the four main steps for turning a quadratic into a 'completed square'?

12) What do you need to do if you divide an inequality by a negative number?

13) What is the four-stage method for graphical inequalities?

14) Write down the steps in the trial and improvement method.

15) Describe how you could solve a quadratic equation using a graph.

16) List the six 'harder' types of graph that you should recognise.

17) Draw the graphs of sin x and cos x over 0-360°.

18) Describe <u>in words</u> and with a sketch the forms of these graphs:
$y = mx + c$;   $y = ax^2 + bx + c$;   $y = ax^3 + bx^2 + cx + d$;   $xy = a$

19) What does the notation $y = f(x)$ mean? Is it really complicated?

20) How many types of shift and stretch are there for graphs?

21) Illustrate each of the different types.

22) Explain how the equation is modified for each of these.

23) Give an example of each type, both the modified equation and a sketch.

24) What is the meaning of life? Why are we here? And why do we have to do so much algebra?

* You'll find answers to these lovely questions on p109.

# Pythagoras' Theorem and Bearings

Pythagoras' theorem sounds hard but it's actually <u>dead simple</u>. It's also dead important, so make sure you really get your teeth into it. Once you've done that there are some tasty bites on <u>bearings</u> to chew on too.

## Pythagoras' Theorem — $a^2 + b^2 = h^2$

1) <u>PYTHAGORAS' THEOREM</u> always goes hand in hand with <u>sin</u>, <u>cos</u> and <u>tan</u> because they're both involved with <u>RIGHT-ANGLED TRIANGLES</u>.

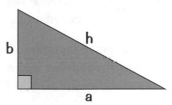

*See p.89 for some sin, cos and tan fun.*

2) The big difference is that Pythagoras does not involve any <u>angles</u> — it just uses <u>two sides</u> to find the <u>third side</u>. (sin, cos and tan always involve <u>ANGLES</u>.)

3) The <u>BASIC FORMULA</u> for Pythagoras is $\boxed{a^2 + b^2 = h^2}$

4) <u>PLUG THE NUMBERS IN</u> and work it out.

5) But get the numbers in the <u>RIGHT PLACE</u>. The 2 shorter sides (squared) add to equal the longest side (squared).

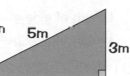

6) Always <u>CHECK</u> that your answer is <u>SENSIBLE</u>.

---

**EXAMPLE:**

"Find the missing side in the triangle shown."

5m    3m

**ANSWER:** $a^2 + b^2 = h^2$

$\therefore 3^2 + x^2 = 5^2$

$\therefore 9 + x^2 = 25$

$\therefore x^2 = 25 - 9 = 16$

$\therefore x = \sqrt{16} = \underline{4\,m}$

(Is it <u>sensible</u>? — Yes, it's shorter than 5 m, but not too much shorter.)

---

## Bearings

To find or plot a bearing you must remember <u>the three key words</u>:

1) **'FROM'** — <u>Find the word 'FROM' in the question</u>, and put your pencil on the diagram at the point you are going '<u>from</u>'.

2) **NORTHLINE** — At the point you are going <u>FROM</u>, <u>draw in a NORTHLINE</u>

3) **CLOCKWISE** — Now draw in the angle CLOCKWISE <u>from the northline to the line joining the two points</u>. This angle is the required bearing.

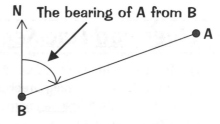

N    The bearing of A from B
● A
B

---

**EXAMPLE:** "Find the bearing of Q <u>from P</u>":

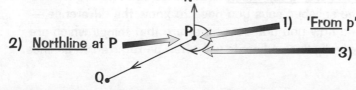

N
P
2) <u>Northline</u> at P
Q

1) 'From p'

3) <u>Clockwise</u>, from the N-line. This angle is the <u>bearing of Q from P</u> and is <u>245°</u>.

N.B. <u>All bearings should be given as 3 figures</u>, e.g. 176°, 034° (not 34°), 005° (not 5°), 018° etc.

---

## Please bear with me while I figure out where we are...

Learn the <u>6 facts about Pythagoras</u> and the <u>3 key words for bearings</u>. Then <u>turn over and scribble 'em down</u>.

1) Find the length of BC.

2) Find the bearing of T from H, by measuring with a protractor.

3) Calculate the <u>back bearing</u> (of H from T).

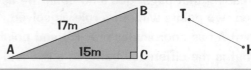

B    T
17m
A    15m    C    H

# Pythagoras, Lines and Line Segments

Pythagoras is a bit of a hero really, how did people ever find the distance between two points without him? Well, probably with some sort of measuring stick — but who needs that when you can wield the power of the mighty right-angled triangle...

## Use Pythagoras to find the Distance Between Points

You need to know how to find the straight-line <u>distance</u> between <u>two points</u> — the trick is to remember <u>Pythagoras</u>...

**EXAMPLE:** "Point P has coordinates (8, 3) and point Q has coordinates (-4, 8). Find the length of the line PQ."

If you get a question like this, follow these rules and it'll all become breathtakingly simple:

1) Draw a <u>sketch</u> to show the <u>right-angled triangle</u>.
2) Find the <u>lengths of the sides</u> of the triangle.
3) <u>Use Pythagoras</u> to find the <u>length of the diagonal</u>. (That's your answer.)

**SOLUTION:** ①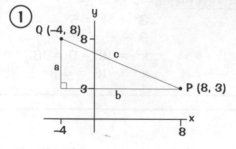

② Length of <u>side a</u> = 8 − 3 = 5
Length of <u>side b</u> = 8 − -4 = 12

③ <u>Use Pythagoras</u> to find <u>side c</u>:
$c^2 = a^2 + b^2 = 5^2 + 12^2 = 25 + 144 = 169$
So: $c = \sqrt{169} = 13$

## Lines and Line Segments...

1) The example above asked you to find the length of the line PQ. To be really precise, the line PQ isn't actually a line — it's a <u>line segment</u>. Confused, read on...

2) A <u>line</u> is <u>straight</u> and continues <u>to infinity</u> (it goes on forever) in both directions.

3) A <u>line segment</u> is just <u>part</u> of a line — it has 2 end points.

4) So the length PQ is just a <u>chunk</u> of the line running through P and Q.

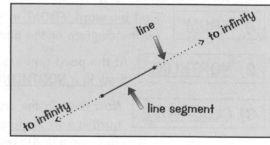

<u>Don't worry too much</u> about lines and line segments. The syllabus says you need to know the difference — and now you do. Just be aware that things which are actually line segments will often be referred to as lines.

*Infinity can never actually be reached, which is just as well because it's a very weird place...*

## Don't go near an angry part of a line — they're segmental...

After reading that page, you'll no doubt be as happy as Larry — the mystery of how to calculate the distance between two points without a ruler is solved. I think we'll all sleep a little easier at night. But before you do....

1) Point A has coordinates (10, 15) and point B has coordinates (6, 12). Find the length of the line AB.
2) What is the difference between a line and a line segment?

# Trigonometry — Sin, Cos, Tan

Trigonometry — it's a big scary word. But it's not a big scary topic. An <u>important</u> topic, yes. An <u>always cropping up</u> topic, definitely. But scary? Pur-lease. Takes more than a triangle to scare me. Read on...

## Method

There are several methods for doing Trig and they're all pretty much the same. However, the method shown below has a number of advantages, mainly because the <u>formula triangles</u> mean the <u>same method</u> is used <u>every time</u>, (no matter which side or angle is being asked for). This makes the whole topic a lot simpler, and you'll find that once you've learned this method, the answers automatically come out right every time.

1) <u>Label</u> the three sides <u>O, A and H</u>
   (Opposite, Adjacent and Hypotenuse).

2) Write down <u>from memory</u> '<u>SOH CAH TOA</u>'.

3) Decide which <u>two sides</u> are <u>involved</u>: O,H  A,H  or
   O,A and select <u>SOH</u>, <u>CAH</u> or <u>TOA</u> accordingly.

4) Turn the one you choose into a <u>FORMULA TRIANGLE</u>:

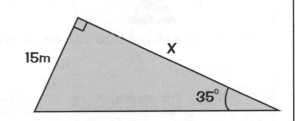

5) <u>Cover up</u> the thing you want to find (with your finger), and write down whatever is left showing.

6) <u>Translate into numbers</u> and work it out.

7) Finally, <u>check</u> that your answer is <u>sensible</u>.

## Four Important Details

1) The <u>Hypotenuse</u> is the <u>LONGEST SIDE</u>. The <u>Opposite</u> is the side <u>OPPOSITE</u> the angle <u>being used</u> ($\theta$), and the <u>Adjacent</u> is the (other) side <u>NEXT TO</u> the angle <u>being used</u>.

2) In the formula triangles, S$\theta$ represents sin $\theta$, C$\theta$ is cos $\theta$, and T$\theta$ is tan $\theta$.

3) Remember, <u>TO FIND THE ANGLE — USE INVERSE</u>. i.e. press [INV] or [SHIFT] or [2nd], followed by <u>sin</u>, <u>cos</u> or <u>tan</u> (and make sure your calculator is in DEG mode).

4) You can only use sin, cos and tan on <u>RIGHT-ANGLED TRIANGLES</u> — you may have to add lines to the diagram to create one, especially with <u>isosceles triangles</u>.

Charlie made one final attempt to preserve the scary reputation of the triangles.

## SOH CAH TOA — the not-so-secret formula for success...

See — not scary at all. All you have to do is <u>learn</u> this one simple method and you'll be SOH-CAH-TOAing along with the best trigonometric minds around. Notice the strategic use of the word "learn" though. It doesn't say "All you have to do is skim briefly over this method and you'll be a trig whizz". No my friend, it doesn't say that. it says "learn". And I shall say it once more for good measure — "learn" this method. And the job's a good-un.

*Unit 3 — Number, Algebra and Geometry 2*

# Trigonometry — Sin, Cos, Tan

Thought you'd been left with no lovely examples to help you through the trials of trig? Not on your nelly...

## Examples:

### EXAMPLE 1:

**"Find x in the triangle shown."**

1) Label O, A, H
2) Write down 'SOH CAH TOA'
3) Two sides <u>involved</u>: O, H
4) So use
5) We want to find H so cover it up to leave: $H = \dfrac{O}{S\theta}$
6) Translate: $x = \dfrac{15}{\sin 35}$

Press 15 ÷ SIN 35 = `26.151702`

So ans = <u>26.2 m</u>

Check it's sensible: yes it's about twice as big as 15, as the diagram suggests.

*(Triangle: Hyp = x, Opp = 15m, angle 35°, Adj)*

### EXAMPLE 2:

**"Find the angle θ in this triangle."**

1) Label O, A, H
2) Write down 'SOH CAH TOA'
3) Two sides <u>involved</u>: A, H
4) So use
5) We want to find θ so cover up Cθ to leave: $C\theta = \dfrac{A}{H}$
6) Translate: $\cos \theta = \dfrac{15}{25} = 0.6$

<u>NOW USE INVERSE:</u>    $\theta = INV \cos (0.6)$

Press INV COS 0.6 = `53.130102`

So ans. = <u>53.1°</u>

Note the usual way of dealing with an <u>ISOSCELES TRIANGLE</u>: split it <u>down the middle</u> to get a <u>RIGHT ANGLE</u>:

*(Triangle: 25m, 25m sides, 30m base, angle θ. Split: Hyp = 25m, Opp, Adj = 15m, angle θ)*

Finally, is it sensible? — Yes, the angle looks about 50°.

---

## Angles of Elevation And Depression

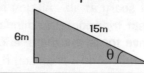

A sad donkey. Poor donkey.

*(Diagram: cliff 16m high, 25m horizontal distance, boat. Angle of DEPRESSION of the boat from the clifftop. Angle of ELEVATION of clifftop from boat.)*

1) The <u>Angle of Depression</u> is the angle <u>downwards</u> from the horizontal.
2) The <u>Angle of Elevation</u> is the angle <u>upwards</u> from the horizontal.
3) The Angles of Elevation and Depression are <u>EQUAL</u>.

---

## The angle of depression — from your eyes to your revision...

Sadly for you, this depressing angle is one you need to be pretty familiar with. So adopt the position and...

1) Find x
2) Find θ
3) Calculate the angles of elevation and depression in the boat drawing above.

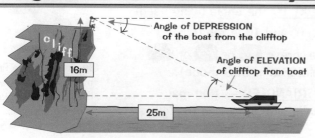

*(Triangle: 15m, x, 28°)*   *(Triangle: 6m, 15m, θ)*

# 3D Pythagoras and Trigonometry

3D questions on Pythagoras and trig are a bit tricky. Or should that be a bit of a trick... for whilst they might <u>seem</u> fiendishly difficult, they're actually mild as a poor quality cheddar. All you need is the same old rules.

## Angle Between Line and Plane — Use a Diagram

### Learn The 3-Step Method

1) Make a <u>RIGHT-ANGLED</u> triangle using <u>the line</u>, <u>a line in the plane</u> and <u>a line between the two</u>.

2) <u>Draw</u> this right-angled triangle again so that you can see it <u>clearly</u>. <u>Label</u> the sides. You might have to use <u>Pythagoras</u> to work out the length of one of the sides.

3) Use <u>trigonometry</u> to calculate the angle.

**EXAMPLE:**

"ABCDE is a square-based pyramid. It is 12 cm high and the square base has sides of length 7 cm. Find the angle the edge AE makes with the base."

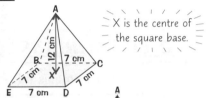

X is the centre of the square base.

1) First draw a <u>right-angled triangle</u> using the <u>edge AE</u>, the <u>base</u> and <u>a line between the two</u> (in this case the central height). Call the angle you're trying to find <u>θ</u>.

2) Now draw this triangle <u>clearly</u> and label it.

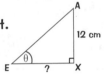

To find θ, you need to know the length of side **EX**.

So, using <u>Pythagoras</u> — $EX^2 = 3.5^2 + 3.5^2 = 24.5 \Rightarrow EX = \sqrt{24.5}$ cm

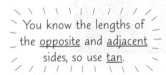

You know the lengths of the <u>opposite</u> and <u>adjacent</u> sides, so use <u>tan</u>.

3) Now use <u>trigonometry</u> to find the angle θ:

$$\tan\theta = \frac{12}{\sqrt{24.5}} = 2.4... \quad \theta = \underline{67.6°} \text{ (1 d.p.)}$$

## Use Right-Angled Triangles To Find Lengths too

**EXAMPLE:** "Find the lengths FH and BH shown in the diagram."

1) First use <u>Pythagoras</u> to find the length <u>FH</u>.

$FH^2 = 3^2 + 3^2 = 18 \Rightarrow FH = \sqrt{18}$ cm

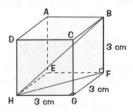

2) Now use <u>Pythagoras</u> again to find the length <u>BH</u>.

$BH^2 = 3^2 + (\sqrt{18})^2 = 27 \Rightarrow BH = \sqrt{27}$ cm $= \underline{5.2 \text{ cm}}$ (1 decimal place)

## Wow — just what can't right-angled triangles do?...

Well, they can't learn this for you. Or bake a victoria sponge. Or answer either of these rather splendid questions. You'll just have to do it yourself.

1) Calculate the angle that the line AG makes with the base of this cuboid.

2) Calculate the length of AG.

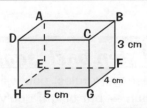

# The Sine and Cosine Rules

Normal trigonometry using **SOH CAH TOA** etc. can only be applied to <u>right-angled</u> triangles. Which leaves us with the question of what to do with other-angled triangles. Step forward the <u>Sine and Cosine Rules</u>...

## Labelling The Triangle

This is very important. You must label the sides and angles properly so that the letters for the sides and angles correspond with each other:

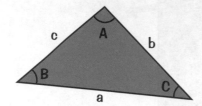

Remember, <u>side 'a' is opposite angle A</u> etc.

It doesn't matter which sides you decide to call a, b, and c, just as long as the angles are then labelled properly.

## Three Formulas to Learn:

These first two formulas let you work out <u>sides</u> and <u>angles</u>:

### The Sine Rule

You don't use the whole thing with both '=' signs of course, so it's not half as bad as it looks — you just choose the two bits that you want:

$$\frac{a}{\sin A} = \frac{b}{\sin B} = \frac{c}{\sin C}$$

e.g. $\dfrac{b}{\sin B} = \dfrac{c}{\sin C}$ or $\dfrac{a}{\sin A} = \dfrac{b}{\sin B}$

### The Cosine Rule

$$a^2 = b^2 + c^2 - 2bc \cos A$$

or $\cos A = \dfrac{b^2 + c^2 - a^2}{2bc}$

### Area of the Triangle

Of course, you already know the simple formula when you have the <u>base</u> and <u>vertical height</u>:

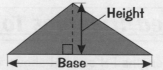

Area = ½ base × height

Well, here's a fancier formula that you can use when you know <u>two sides</u> and the angle <u>between them</u>:

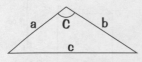

<u>Area of triangle = ½ ab sin C</u>

You need to <u>**LEARN**</u> all of these formulas off by heart and practise using them.
If you don't, you won't be able to use them in the Exam, even if they give them to you.

## ...and step back again. Hope you enjoyed your moment in the spotlight...

With these extra rules, you will be able to conquer any triangles you come across. The next step is surely world domination — but only if you've learnt the formulas on this page and know how to properly label a triangle.

# The Sine and Cosine Rules

Amazingly, there are only <u>FOUR</u> question types where the <u>Sine</u> and <u>Cosine</u> rules would be applied. So learn the exact details of these four examples and you'll be laughing. WARNING: if you laugh too much people will think you're crazy.

## The Four Examples

You might get any of these types of question in 3D but <u>DON'T PANIC!</u>
You answer them in <u>exactly</u> the same way as you would if they were in 2D.

### TWO ANGLES given plus ANY SIDE    — SINE RULE NEEDED

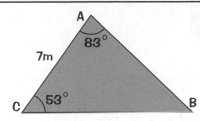

1) Don't forget the obvious: $B = 180 - 83 - 53 = \underline{44^0}$

2) Then use $\dfrac{b}{\sin B} = \dfrac{c}{\sin C} \Rightarrow \dfrac{7}{\sin 44} = \dfrac{c}{\sin 53}$

3) Which gives $\Rightarrow c = \dfrac{7 \times \sin 53}{\sin 44} = \underline{8.05\,m}$

The rest is easy using the SINE RULE

### TWO SIDES given plus an ANGLE NOT ENCLOSED by them    — SINE RULE NEEDED

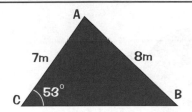

1) Use: $\dfrac{b}{\sin B} = \dfrac{c}{\sin C} \Rightarrow \dfrac{7}{\sin B} = \dfrac{8}{\sin 53}$

2) $\Rightarrow \sin B = \dfrac{7 \times \sin 53}{8} = 0.6988 \Rightarrow B = \sin^{-1}(0.6988) = \underline{44.3^0}$

The rest is easy using the SINE RULE

### TWO SIDES given plus THE ANGLE ENCLOSED by them    — COSINE RULE NEEDED

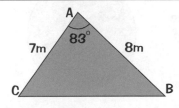

1) Use: $a^2 = b^2 + c^2 - 2bc \cos A$
$= 7^2 + 8^2 - 2 \times 7 \times 8 \times \cos 83$
$= 99.3506 \Rightarrow a = \sqrt{99.3506} = \underline{9.97\,m}$

The rest is easy using the SINE RULE

### ALL THREE SIDES given but NO ANGLES    — COSINE RULE NEEDED

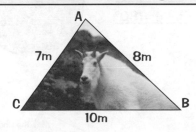

1) Use: $\cos A = \dfrac{b^2 + c^2 - a^2}{2bc}$
$= \dfrac{49 + 64 - 100}{2 \times 7 \times 8} = \dfrac{13}{112} = 0.11607$

2) Hence $A = \cos^{-1}(0.11607) = \underline{83.3^0}$    The rest is easy using the SINE RULE

## Four examples + three formulas + two rules = one trigonometric genius...

And that genius'll be you. So get to it — learn the page, ace your exam, live with success and joy. Aaah.

1) Write down <u>a new version</u> of each of the 4 examples above and then use the SINE and COSINE RULES to find <u>ALL of the sides and angles</u> for each one.

2) A triangle has two sides of 12 m and 17 m with an angle of $70^0$ between them. Find all the other sides and angles in the triangle. (A sketch is essential, of course).

# More Circle Geometry

Bet you've always thought there's not much to know about circles. No corners, no angles... or so you thought. Well folks, grab your map and compass, as there's a whole lot more to discover. We're going in...

## 6 Simple Rules — That's all:

You'll need the circle rules you learnt in Unit 2 as well — have a peek back at p.60 if you've forgotten them.

### 1) Angle in a Semicircle = 90°

A triangle drawn from the <u>two ends of a diameter</u> will **ALWAYS** make an <u>angle of 90° where it hits</u> the edge of the circle, no matter where it hits.

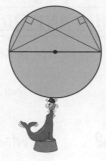

### 2) Chord Bisector is a Diameter

A <u>CHORD</u> is any line <u>drawn across a circle</u>. And no matter where you draw a chord, the line that <u>cuts it exactly in half</u> (at 90°), will <u>go through the centre of the circle</u> and so will be a <u>DIAMETER</u>.

CHORD
(Cut in two)

O

### 3) Angles in the Same Segment Are Equal

All triangles drawn from a chord will have <u>the same angle where they touch the circle</u>. Also, the two angles on opposite sides of the chord <u>add up to 180°</u>.

Chord

a+b = 180°

### 4) Angle at the Centre is Twice the Angle at the Edge

The angle subtended at the centre of a circle is <u>**EXACTLY DOUBLE**</u> the angle subtended at the edge of the circle from the same two points (two ends of the same chord). The phrase '<u>angle subtended at</u>' is nothing complicated, it's just a bit posher than saying '<u>angle made at</u>'.

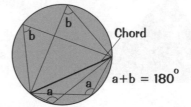

a

2a

### 5) Opposite Angles of a Cyclic Quadrilateral Add Up to 180°

A <u>cyclic quadrilateral</u> is a <u>4-sided shape with every corner touching the circle</u>. Both pairs of opposite angles add up to 180°.

<u>a+c=180°</u>

<u>b+d=180°</u>

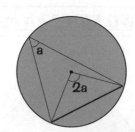

a

b

d

c

### 6) Angle in Opposite Segment is Equal

This is perhaps the trickiest one to remember. If you draw a <u>tangent</u> and a <u>chord</u> that meet, then <u>the angle between them</u> is always <u>equal</u> to '<u>the angle in the opposite segment</u>' (i.e. the angle made at the edge of the circle by two lines drawn from the chord).

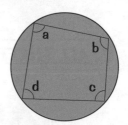

The Opposite Segment (white)

The Chord

b

Angle in the opposite segment

b

Angle between chord and tangent

## Might do a spot of angling after lunch...

You can join me if you like — but you need to learn all about circles first. SOOooo, I suggest you do this:

1) Turn over the page and write down all six rules from memory.

# Vectors

Three monstrously important things you need to know about <u>vectors</u>. Monsters... Aaaaaarrrrgggghhhh...

## The Four Notations

The vector shown here can be referred to as:

or <u>a</u> or **a** <sub>(in bold type)</sub> or $\overrightarrow{AB}$

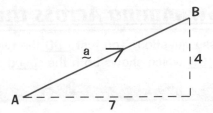

It's pretty obvious what these mean. Just make sure you know which is which in the column vector (x→ and y↑ ) and what a negative value means in a column vector.

## Adding And Subtracting Vectors

Vectors must always be added <u>end to end</u>, so that the <u>arrows all point with</u> each other, <u>not against</u> each other.

The vector you get from adding two other vectors together is called the <u>RESULTANT</u>.

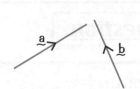

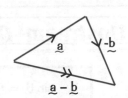

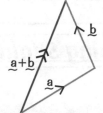

Adding and subtracting <u>COLUMN VECTORS</u> is really easy:

E.g. if $\underline{a} = \begin{pmatrix} 5 \\ 3 \end{pmatrix}$ and $\underline{b} = \begin{pmatrix} -2 \\ 4 \end{pmatrix}$ then $2\underline{a} - \underline{b} = 2\begin{pmatrix} 5 \\ 3 \end{pmatrix} - \begin{pmatrix} -2 \\ 4 \end{pmatrix} = \begin{pmatrix} 12 \\ 2 \end{pmatrix}$

## A Typical Exam Question

This is a common type of question and it illustrates a very important vector technique:

> To obtain the <u>unknown vector</u> just '<u>get there</u>' by any route <u>made up of known vectors</u>

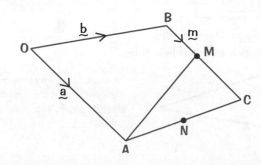

Applying this rule we can easily obtain the following vectors in term of $\underline{a}$, $\underline{b}$ and $\underline{m}$ (given that M and N are mid points):

$\overrightarrow{AM} = -\underline{a} + \underline{b} + \underline{m}$  (i.e. get there via O and B)

$\overrightarrow{OC} = \underline{b} + 2\underline{m}$  (i.e. get there via B and M)

$\overrightarrow{AC} = -\underline{a} + \underline{b} + 2\underline{m}$  (A to C via O, B and M)

## From numpty to vector king — via R, E, V, I, S, I, O and N...

I know it's dull, but make sure you know the vector basics (and the page doesn't look like a bunch of randomly surfing letters), then real life won't seem so bad. Or real life vectors, which is the next fun page. Now try these:

1) For the diagram above, express the following in terms of $\underline{a}$, $\underline{b}$ and $\underline{m}$:
   a) $\overrightarrow{MO}$   b) $\overrightarrow{AN}$   c) $\overrightarrow{BN}$   d) $\overrightarrow{NM}$

*Unit 3 — Number, Algebra and Geometry 2*

# "Real Life" Vector Questions

These are the type of vector question you're most likely to stumble across in the exam, so make sure you learn all the little tricks on this page. They'll stop you coming a cropper. Or at least reduce the chances of it.

## The Old 'Swimming Across the River' Question

This is a really easy question: You just <u>ADD</u> the two velocity vectors <u>END TO END</u> and draw the <u>RESULTANT VECTOR</u> which shows both the <u>speed</u> and <u>direction</u> of the final course. Simple huh?

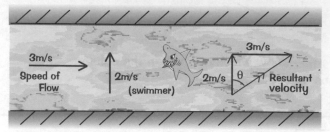

Overall Speed $= \sqrt{3^2 + 2^2}$
$= \sqrt{13} = 3.6$m/s
Direction: $\tan\theta = 3 \div 2$
$\theta = \tan^{-1}(1.5) = 56.3°$

As usual with vectors, you'll need to use <u>Pythagoras and Trig</u> to find the length and angle, but that's no big deal is it? Just make sure you LEARN the two methods in this question. The example shown above is absolutely bog-standard stuff and you should definitely see it that way, rather than as one random question of which there may be hundreds — there aren't!

## The Old 'Swimming Slightly Upstream' Question

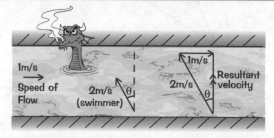

1) $\sin\theta = \text{OPP}/\text{HYP}$
$= 1/2$
so $\theta = \sin^{-1}(0.5) = 30°$

2) <u>Speed</u> $= \sqrt{2^2 - 1^2} = \sqrt{3} = 1.73$ m/s

The general idea here is to end up going <u>directly across the river</u>, and once again the old faithful method of drawing a <u>vector triangle</u> makes light work of the whole thing — 2 vectors joined end to end to give the resultant velocity. However, in this case the resultant is drawn in <u>first</u> (straight across), so that the angle θ has to be worked out <u>to fit</u> as shown above.

## The Old 'Queen Mary's Tugboats' Question

The problem here is to find the overall force from the two tugs.

This is tackled by <u>adding</u> the vectors <u>end to end</u> to produce a triangle like this:

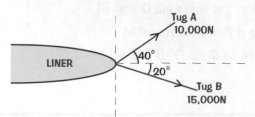

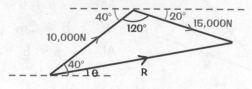

The angle 120° inside the triangle is found using the rules for <u>alternate angles</u> and angles on a <u>straight line</u> — see P57-58.

You then need to use the <u>SINE & COSINE RULES</u> to find R and θ (the size and direction of the resultant force).

## The old 'learn everything on this page' bit...

Learn the 3 examples on this page, then <u>turn over and write them out</u>, but with <u>different numbers</u>. Ah, time for...

1) Work out the overall force on the Queen Mary in example 3 (by finding R and θ).

# The Four Transformations

**T** ranslation — ONE Detail
**E** nlargement — TWO Details
**R** otation — THREE Details
**R** eflection — ONE Detail
**Y**

1) Use the name **TERRY** to remember the 4 types.
2) You must always specify **all the details** for each type.
3) It'll help if you remember which properties remain **unchanged** in each transformation, too.

## 1) TRANSLATION

You must **specify this ONE detail**:

1) The **VECTOR OF TRANSLATION** $\left(\begin{array}{c} x \to \\ y \updownarrow \end{array}\right)$ (See P.95 on vector notation)

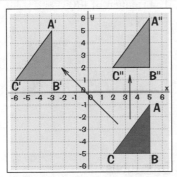

ABC to A'B'C' is a translation of $\begin{pmatrix} -8 \\ 6 \end{pmatrix}$

ABC to A''B''C'' is a translation of $\begin{pmatrix} 0 \\ 7 \end{pmatrix}$

All that changes in a translation is the **POSITION** of the object — **everything else** remains **unchanged**.

## 2) ENLARGEMENT

You must **specify these 2 details**:

1) The **SCALE FACTOR**
2) The **CENTRE** of Enlargement

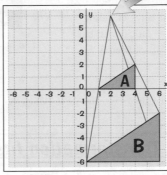 

From **A to B** is an enlargement of **scale factor 2**, and **centre (2,6)**

From **B to A** is an enlargement of **scale factor 1/2** and **centre (2,6)**

The **ANGLES** of the object and **RATIOS** of the lengths remain **unchanged**. The **ORIENTATION** is unchanged unless the scale factor is negative.

## 3) ROTATION

You must **specify these 3 details**:

1) **ANGLE** turned
2) **DIRECTION** (Clockwise or...)
3) **CENTRE** of Rotation

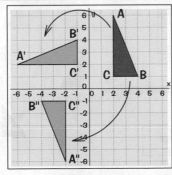

ABC to A'B'C' is a Rotation of **90°**, **anticlockwise**, **ABOUT the origin**.

ABC to A''B''C'' is a Rotation of **half a turn (180°)**, **clockwise**, **ABOUT the origin**.

The only things that change in a rotation are the **POSITION** and the **ORIENTATION** of the object. **Everything else** remains **unchanged**.

## 4) REFLECTION

You must **specify this ONE detail**:

1) The **MIRROR LINE**

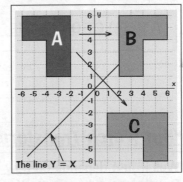

A to B is a **reflection in the y-axis**.

A to C is a **reflection in the line y = x**

The line Y = X

With reflection, the **POSITION** and **ORIENTATION** of the object are the **only things that change**.

---

## _Moving eet to ze left — a perfect translation..._

Get it? Nice. Learn the names of the **four transformations** and the details that go with each. When you think you know it, **turn over and write it all down**.
Now you're ready for this lovely question:

1) Describe **fully** these transformations: A → B, B → C, C → A, A → D.

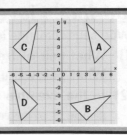

# The Four Transformations

In Exam questions they'll often do something <u>horrid</u> like <u>stick two transformations together</u> and then ask you what combination gets you from shape A to shape B. Be <u>ready</u> — those examiners are brutal.

## The Better You Know Them All — The Easier it is

These kinds of question aren't so bad — but <u>ONLY</u> if you've <u>LEARNT</u> the <u>four transformations</u> on the last page <u>really well</u> — if you don't know them, then you certainly won't do too well at spotting a <u>combination</u> of one followed by another. That's because the method is basically <u>try it and see...</u>

### Example:

"What combination of two transformations takes you from triangle A to triangle B?"

(There's usually a few different ways of getting from one shape to the other — but remember you only need to find <u>ONE</u> of them.)

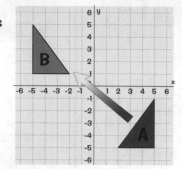

### Method:

**SLIGHTLY WEIRD CASE:**
An <u>ENLARGEMENT</u> with a <u>NEGATIVE SCALE FACTOR</u> looks like two transformations:

If the <u>scale factor is NEGATIVE</u> the shape pops out the other side of the enlargement centre — so it looks like an enlargement <u>and</u> a rotation. If the scale factor is -1, it's exactly the same as a rotation of 180°.

A to B is an enlargement of scale factor -2. B to A is an enlargement of scale factor -½.

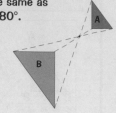

### Try an Obvious Transformation first, and See...

If you <u>think</u> about it, the answer can <u>only</u> be a combination of two of the <u>four types</u> shown on the last page, so you can immediately start to <u>narrow it down</u>:

1)  Since the shapes are the <u>same size</u> we can <u>rule out enlargements</u>.

2)  Next, <u>try a reflection</u> (in either the x-axis or the y-axis). Here we've tried a reflection in the <u>y-axis</u>, to give shape A':

3)  You should now easily be able to see the <u>final step</u> from A' to B — it's a <u>translation</u> of $\begin{pmatrix} 0 \\ 6 \end{pmatrix}$.

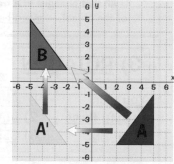

And that's it <u>DONE</u> — from A to B is simply a combination of:

> A <u>REFLECTION IN THE Y-AXIS</u> followed by a <u>TRANSLATION OF</u> $\begin{pmatrix} 0 \\ 6 \end{pmatrix}$

At least that's <u>one answer</u> anyway. If instead we decided to reflect it in the <u>x-axis</u> first (as shown here) then we'd get another answer (see question 2 below) — but both are right.

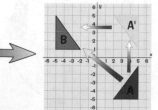

### "But Which Transformation do I try first?" I hear you cry

Well it just depends on <u>how it looks</u>.
But the <u>more transformation questions</u> you do, the more obvious that first guess becomes.
In other words: the more you <u>practise</u>, the <u>easier</u> you'll be able to do it — surprise surprise...

## Darling, I love how the moonlight reflects in your y-axis...

Who says romance is dead? Anyway, enough luvvy-duvvy stuff — crack on and learn this page.

1)  What pair of transformations will convert shape C into shape D?
    What pair will convert shape D to shape C?

2)  In the example above, find the other transformation needed to get to shape B after reflecting shape A in the x-axis.

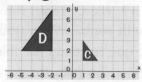

# Congruence and Similarity

<u>Congruence</u> is another ridiculous maths word which sounds really complicated when it's not:
If two shapes are congruent, they are simply <u>the same</u> — the <u>same size</u> and the <u>same shape</u>.
That's all it is.  They can however be <u>mirror images</u>.

## CONGRUENT
— same size,
same shape

## SIMILAR
— same shape,
<u>different size</u>

Note that the angles
are always unchanged

## Congruent Triangles — are they or aren't they?

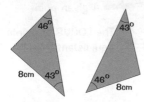

Probably the <u>trickiest area</u> of congruence is deciding whether
<u>two triangles</u>, like the ones shown here, are <u>CONGRUENT</u>.

In other words, from the skimpy information given, are the two going
to be the same or different.  There are <u>THREE IMPORTANT STEPS</u>:

1)  The Golden Rule is definitely to
    <u>draw them both</u> in the <u>same orientation</u>
    — only then can you compare them properly:

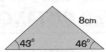

2)  <u>Don't jump to hasty conclusions</u> — although the 8 cm sides are clearly in different positions,
    it's always possible that <u>both top sides are 8 cm</u>.  In this case we can work out that they're <u>not</u>
    because the angles are different (so they can't be isosceles).

3)  Now see if any of these <u>conditions are true</u>.  If <u>ONE</u> of the conditions holds,
    the triangles are <u>congruent</u>.

| | | |
|---|---|---|
| 1) | SSS | three sides are the same |
| 2) | AAS | two angles and a side match up |
| 3) | SAS | two sides and the angle between them match up |
| 4) | RHS | a right angle, the hypotenuse (longest side) and one other side all match up |

For two triangles to be congruent, <u>ONE OR MORE</u> of these four conditions must hold.

(<u>If none are true</u>, then you have proof
that the triangles <u>aren't congruent</u>.)

## Congruence and Transformations

WHEN A SHAPE IS <u>TRANSLATED</u>, <u>ROTATED</u> OR <u>REFLECTED</u>,
THE IMAGE IS CONGRUENT TO THE ORIGINAL SHAPE.
<u>ENLARGEMENTS</u> DON'T FOLLOW THIS RULE.

E.g.

A to B is a <u>translation</u> of $\begin{pmatrix} -8 \\ -1 \end{pmatrix}$.
The lengths and angles
are unchanged, so <u>A is congruent to B</u>.

E.g.

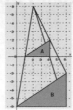

A to B is an <u>enlargement</u> of scale
factor 2, and centre (2, 6).

The angles are unchanged
but not the lengths, so
<u>A is not congruent to B</u>.

## Now, where did I put that cup of tea...

Ah there it is over there.  Lovely.  So here's the bad news — you need to know everything
on this page.  And the good news — it'll all be great fun.  What... you don't believe me?
<u>When you think you know it</u>, turn the page over and <u>write it all down</u> from <u>memory</u>,
including the sketches and examples.

They're my biscuits.  Hands off.

# Loci and Construction

A <u>LOCUS</u> (another ridiculous maths word) is simply:

## A LINE that shows <u>all the points which fit in with a given rule</u>.

Make sure you learn how to do these <u>PROPERLY</u> using a <u>ruler</u> and <u>compasses</u> as shown on these two pages.

**1)**
### The locus of points which are '<u>A FIXED DISTANCE from a given POINT</u>'

This locus is simply a <u>CIRCLE</u>.

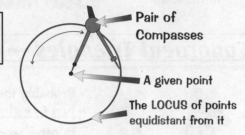

Pair of Compasses

A given point

The LOCUS of points equidistant from it

**2)**
### The locus of points which are '<u>A FIXED DISTANCE from a given LINE</u>'

This locus is an <u>OVAL SHAPE</u>.

It has <u>straight sides</u> (drawn with a <u>ruler</u>) and <u>ends</u> which are <u>perfect semicircles</u> (drawn with compasses).

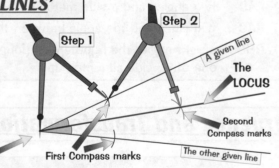

Semicircle ends drawn with compasses

A given line

The LOCUS of points equidistant from it

**3)**
### The locus of points which are '<u>EQUIDISTANT from TWO GIVEN LINES</u>'

1) Keep the compass setting <u>THE SAME</u> while you make <u>all four marks</u>.

2) Make sure you <u>leave</u> your compass marks <u>showing</u>.

3) You get <u>two equal angles</u> — i.e. this <u>LOCUS</u> is actually an <u>ANGLE BISECTOR</u>.

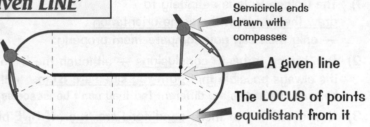

Step 2

Step 1

A given line

The LOCUS

Second Compass marks

The other given line

First Compass marks

**4)**
### The locus of points which are '<u>EQUIDISTANT from TWO GIVEN POINTS</u>'

(In the diagram below, A and B are the two given points.)

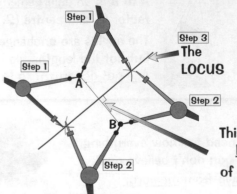

Step 1

Step 1

Step 3

Step 2

Step 2

The LOCUS

A

B

<u>This LOCUS</u> is all points which are the <u>same</u> <u>distance</u> from A as they are from B.

This time the locus is actually the <u>PERPENDICULAR BISECTOR</u> of the line joining the two points.

# Loci and Construction

Don't just read the page through once and hope you'll remember it — get your ruler, compasses and pencil out and have a go. It's the only way of testing whether you really know this stuff.

## Constructing accurate 60° angles

1) They may well ask you to draw an <u>accurate 60° angle</u>.

2) One thing they're needed for is drawing <u>equilateral triangles</u>.

3) Make sure you <u>follow the method</u> shown in this diagram, and that you can do it <u>entirely from memory</u>.

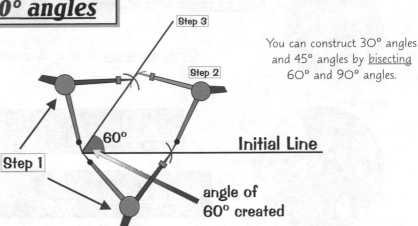

You can construct 30° angles and 45° angles by <u>bisecting</u> 60° and 90° angles.

## Constructing accurate 90° angles

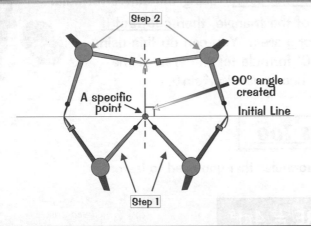

1) They might want you to draw an <u>accurate 90° angle</u>.

2) They won't accept it just done <u>'by eye'</u> or with a ruler — if you want the marks you've got to do it <u>the proper way</u> with <u>compasses</u> like I've shown you here.

3) Make sure you can <u>follow the method</u> shown in this diagram.

## Drawing the Perpendicular from a Point to a Line

1) This is similar to the one above but <u>not quite the same</u> — make sure you can do <u>both</u>.

2) Again, they won't accept it just done <u>'by eye'</u> or with a ruler — you've got to do it <u>the proper way</u> with <u>compasses</u>.

3) <u>Learn</u> the diagram.

If you need to draw a parallel line, just draw <u>a second line perpendicular to the first one you drew</u>.

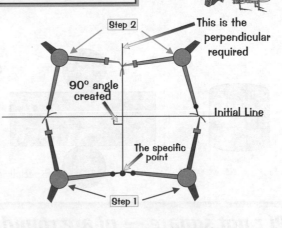

## Horrid pesky little Loci...

Loci and constructions aren't too bad really. After all, you get to draw and to use some exciting high tech equipment. So anyway, here we go again with the tasky bit. Cover up the pages and draw an example of each of the four loci. Also draw an equilateral triangle and a square with accurate 60° and 90° angles.
Finally, draw a line and a point and construct the perpendicular from the point to the line. Ah, go on.

# Circles, Cylinders and Spheres

## Learn these Formulas for Circle Areas

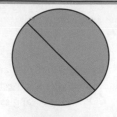

The area of a semi-circle is just half the area of the full circle.

Area of circle = π × (radius)²

$$A = \pi \times r^2$$

Circumference = π × diameter

$$C = \pi \times D$$

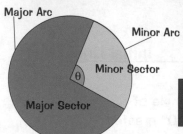

Major Arc

Minor Arc

Minor Sector

θ

Major Sector

Area of Sector = $\dfrac{\theta}{360}$ × Area of full Circle

(Pretty obvious really isn't it?)

Length of Arc = $\dfrac{\theta}{360}$ × Circumference of full Circle

(Obvious again, no?)

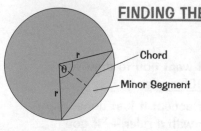

r

θ

r

Chord

Minor Segment

**FINDING THE AREA OF A SEGMENT** is OK if you know the formulas:

1) Find the <u>area of the sector</u> using the above formula.
2) Find the area of the triangle, then <u>subtract it</u> from the sector's area. You can do this using the '½ ab sin C' formula for the area of the triangle which becomes: ½ r²sin θ.

## And these Surface Area Formulas Too

<u>SPHERES, CYLINDERS AND CONES</u> have surface area formulas that you need to learn:

r

**Surface area of a SPHERE = 4πr²**

curved area of cone

area of circular base

ℓ

r

**Surface area of a CONE = πrl + πr²**

h

Cylinder

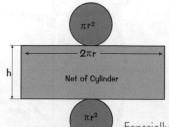

πr²

2πr

h

Net of Cylinder

πr²

**Surface area of a CYLINDER = 2πrh + 2πr²**

Especially note that <u>the length of the rectangle</u> is equal to the <u>circumference</u> of the circular ends.

## <u>Pi r not square — pi are round. Pi are tasty...</u>

Right, nothing too scary on this page — just a load of formulas to learn. Plain and simple.
And once you've got them all learned, have a crack at this question.

1) <u>Find the perimeter and area of this shape.</u> As you should certainly expect for any Exam question on area, you will need to make use of <u>Pythagoras</u> and/or <u>trigonometry</u> to solve this one. (See p87-91.)

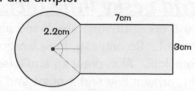

2.2cm

7cm

3cm

# Circles, Cylinders and Spheres

This page has a great bonus — once you've learnt it you can amaze people by calculating the volume of their ice cream cones. Who says revision isn't fun. I love it. I take exams just for fun.

## 1) Sphere

A hemisphere is just half a sphere — so its volume is half the volume of the full sphere.

Sounds like a load of balls to me

$$\text{VOLUME OF SPHERE} = \frac{4}{3}\pi r^3$$

<u>EXAMPLE</u>: The moon has a radius of 1700 km, find its volume.

<u>Ans</u>: $V = \frac{4}{3}\pi r^3 = \frac{4}{3} \times 3.14 \times 1700^3 = 2.1 \times 10^{10}$ km$^3$     (A lot of cheese)

## 2) Cylinders

A cylinder is just a "circular prism", so its volume is just:

$$\text{VOLUME OF CYLINDER} = \pi r^2 \times \text{LENGTH}$$

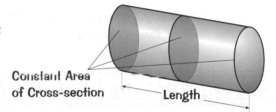

Constant Area of Cross-section — Length

## 3) Cones

A pyramid is any shape that goes <u>up to a point at the top</u>. Its base can be any shape at all. If the base is a circle then it's called a <u>cone</u> (rather than a circular pyramid).

Cone

$$\text{VOLUME OF CONE} = \frac{1}{3} \times \pi r^2 \times \text{HEIGHT}$$

This surprisingly simple formula is true for any cone, whether it goes up 'vertically' (like the one shown here) or off to one side (like the one at the bottom of the page).

## 4) A Frustum is Part of a Cone

A <u>frustum of a cone</u> is what's left when the top part of a cone is cut off parallel to its circular base

$$\begin{array}{c} \text{VOLUME OF} \\ \text{FRUSTUM} \end{array} = \begin{array}{c} \text{VOLUME OF THE} \\ \text{ORIGINAL CONE} \end{array} - \begin{array}{c} \text{VOLUME OF THE} \\ \text{REMOVED CONE} \end{array}$$

$$= \frac{1}{3}\pi R^2 H - \frac{1}{3}\pi r^2 h$$

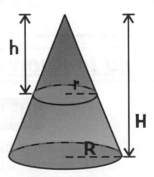

## No mum, a cone isn't 'just as good' — all the other Pharaohs will laugh at me...

Go on, have a go... Get out there, buy an ice cream and get your ruler out. But first...

1) Name the shape to the right and find its volume.
2) A ping pong ball has a diameter of 4 cm.
   A tennis ball has a diameter of 7 cm.
   Find the volume of both balls.

4m

2.2m

# Area, Volume and Density

## Areas and Volumes of Enlargements

Ho ho! This little joker catches everybody out. The increase in area and volume is <u>BIGGER</u> than the scale factor.

<u>For example</u>, if the <u>Scale Factor is 2</u>, the lengths are <u>twice as big</u>, each area is <u>4 times</u> as big, and the volume is <u>8 times</u> as big.

The rule is this:

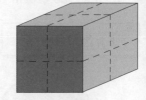

| For a <u>SCALE FACTOR N</u>: | | Or... expressed <u>AS RATIOS</u>: | | |
|---|---|---|---|---|
| The <u>SIDES</u> are | N times bigger | Lengths | a : b | e.g. 3 : 4 |
| The <u>AREAS</u> are | $N^2$ times bigger | Areas | $a^2 : b^2$ | e.g. 9 : 16 |
| The <u>VOLUMES</u> are | $N^3$ times bigger | Volumes | $a^3 : b^3$ | e.g. 27 : 64 |

Simple... but <u>VERY FORGETTABLE</u>

<u>EXAMPLE</u>:

2 spheres have surface areas of $16 \, m^2$ and $25 \, m^2$. Find the ratio of their volumes.

<u>ANS</u>: 16 : 25 is the areas ratio which must be $a^2 : b^2$,
i.e. $a^2 : b^2 = 16 : 25$
and so a : b = 4 : 5
and so $a^3 : b^3 = \underline{64 : 125}$ — the volumes ratio.

## Converting Area and Volume Measurements

$$1 \, m^2 = 100 \, cm \times 100 \, cm = 10\,000 \, cm^2$$

1) To change area measurements from $m^2$ to $cm^2$ multiply the area in $m^2$ by 10 000 (e.g. $3 \, m^2 = 30\,000 \, cm^2$).

2) To change area measurements from $cm^2$ to $m^2$ divide the area in $cm^2$ by 10 000 (e.g. $45\,000 \, cm^2 = 4.5 \, m^2$).

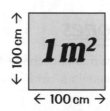

$1 \, m^2$ (← 100 cm →, ↑ 100 cm ↓)

$$1 \, m^3 = 100 \, cm \times 100 \, cm \times 100 \, cm = 1\,000\,000 \, cm^3$$

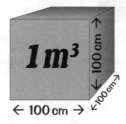

$1 \, m^3$ (← 100 cm →, ← 100 cm, ← 100 cm)

1) To change volume measurements from $m^3$ to $cm^3$ multiply the volume in $m^3$ by 1 000 000 (e.g. $3 \, m^3 = 3\,000\,000 \, cm^3$).

2) To change volume measurements from $cm^3$ to $m^3$ divide the volume in $cm^3$ by 1 000 000 (e.g. $4\,500\,000 \, cm^3 = 4.5 \, m^3$).

## You Need to Know How to Work Out Density

### DENSITY = MASS ÷ VOLUME

You can put the above formula for it into a formula triangle like this:

You might think this is physics, but density is specifically mentioned in the maths syllabus.

One way or another you <u>MUST</u> remember this formula for density, because they promise nothing and without it you'll be stuck. The best method by far is to <u>remember the order of the letters</u> in the formula triangle as $D^MV$ or <u>DiMoV</u> (The Russian Agent!).

> **Example:**
>
> "Find the volume of an object with a mass of 40g and a density of $6.4 \, g/cm^3$."
>
> To find volume, <u>cover up V</u>. This leaves M/D, <u>so V = M ÷ D = 40 ÷ 6.4 = 6.25 $cm^3$</u>.

# Revision Summary for Unit 3 — Part 2

Here we are again — more lovely questions for you to test yourself with.

Remember you have to keep practising these questions <u>over and over again</u> until you can answer them <u>all</u>. Seriously, you do. That's the best kind of revision there is because the whole idea is to find out what you <u>don't know</u> and then learn it <u>until you do</u>. Enjoy.

## KEEP LEARNING THESE BASIC FACTS UNTIL YOU KNOW THEM

1)  What is the formula for Pythagoras' theorem? Where can you use Pythagoras?

2)  How do you decide which numbers go where? What final check do you make?

3)* A museum has a flight of stairs up to its front door (see diagram). 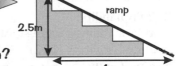 A ramp is to be put over the top of the steps for wheelchair users. Calculate the length that the ramp would need to be.

4)  What are the three key words for bearings? How must bearings be written?

5)  Describe how to find the length of a line, given the coordinates of the endpoints.

6)  Write down the important steps of a good solid method for doing TRIG.

7)  What are the advantages of using formula triangles to do sin, cos and tan?

8)* Most avalanches happen on slopes that are at angles of between 15° and 60°. Jane decided to estimate the angle of the slope she was on to see whether she was at high risk from an avalanche. She created a right-angled triangle using two ice axes and estimated the measurements shown. Calculate angle x — the angle of the slope.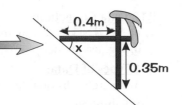

9)  Draw a diagram to illustrate angles of elevation and depression.

10) What three steps allow you to find the angle between a line and a plane?

11) Write down the SINE and COSINE RULES and draw a properly labelled triangle.

12) List the 4 different types of sine/cosine rule questions and which rule you need for each.

13) What is the formula (involving sin) for the area of any triangle? Demonstrate its use.

14) Write down the six simple rules for circle geometry.

15) What are the four vector notations?

16) What's the main rule for adding vectors?

17) In a typical Exam question, what is the basic rule for finding an unknown vector?

18) Produce your own 'swimming across the river' question and work it out.

19) Produce your own 'swimming slightly upstream' question and work it out.

20) Produce your own 'Queen Mary's tugboats' question and do it using the SINE and COSINE rules.

21) List the four types of transformation. What details must be specified for each type?

22) What do "congruent" and "similar" mean?

23) What are the rules for deciding if two triangles are congruent or not?

24) Demonstrate how to accurately draw the bisector of an angle.

25) Demonstrate how to accurately draw the perpendicular bisector of a line.

26) Demonstrate how to draw accurate 60° angles. Draw an accurate equilateral triangle.

27) Demonstrate how to draw accurate 90° angles. Draw an accurate square.

28) What is the formula for the length of an arc? Which other formula is similar?

29) What are the three steps needed to find the area of a segment?

30)* A confectionery company is designing the packaging for a new brand of biscuits. The packaging will be cylindrical, with a diameter of 4 cm and a height of 15 cm. Calculate the surface area of the packaging.

31)* Geoff has built a scale model of a garden shed that he hopes to supply to garden centres. His model is 30 cm wide, 60 cm long and 50 cm high. He has used a scale factor of 0.2. Give the width, length and height of the actual sheds.

*Looking for answers? Head on over to p109.

# Answers

## Unit 1

**P.4 Fractions, Decimals and Percentages:** **1) a)** 6/10 = 3/5 **b)** 2/100 = 1/50 **c)** 77/100
**d)** 555/1000 = 111/200 **e)** 56/10 = 28/5

**P.5 Percentages:** **1)** 12.5% **2)** £14 350 **3)** 1.39%

**P.6 Compound Interest and Depreciation:** **1)** 48 stick insects **2)** 0.15 m/s. Forever.

**P.8 Ratios:** **1) a)** 5:7 **b)** 2:3 **c)** 3:5 **2)** 17½ bowls of porridge **3)** £3500 : £2100 : £2800

**P.9 Rounding and Estimating:** **1)** Surface area approx 600 miles × 150 miles = 90 000 square miles
Can of beans volume approx 7 cm × 7 cm × 10 cm = 490 cm³ **2)** 3.57 **3)** 12.91

**P.10 Rounding and Estimating:** **1) a)** 3.41 **b)** 1.05 **c)** 0.07 **d)** 3.60
**2 a)** 568 **b)** 23400 **c)** 0.0456 **d)** 0.909

**P.12 Probability:**
**1) a)** Probability = QQA+QAQ+AQQ = (4/52)(3/51)(1/50) + (4/52)(1/51)(3/50) + (1/52)(4/51)(3/50) = 3/11050
**b)** Probability = (4/52) × (3/51) + (4/52) × (3/51) + (4/52) × (3/51) = 3 × (4/52) × (3/51) = 3/221

**P.13 Probability — Relative Frequency:**
**1)** Probability of Bill drawing an ace = (13/100) = 0.13 Expected probability of drawing an ace = (4/52) = 0.077.
0.13 is much greater than 0.077 so YES, the pack is probably biased.

**P.14 Probability — Tree Diagrams:**
**2)** 8/15

**P.15 Probability — Tree Diagrams:**
**1)** (2/7) × (1/6) × (5/6) × (4/5) = (40/1260) = (2/63)

**P.17 Data Collection:**
**1) a)** Need to know how many people have school dinners each day of the week.
**b)** E.g. asking people when they have school dinner or observing how many people do on each day.

**P.18 Types of Data:**
**1) a)** discrete **b)** qualitative **c)** qualitative **d)** continuous

**P.19 Sampling:**
**1)** The sample frame is a list of all the people registered at the surgery.
**2)** No, because it is only sampling one year in the school and music tastes might be different in different year groups.

**P.20 Sampling Methods:**
**1)** 1 manager, 2 middle managers and 7 shop-floor workers.

**P.21 Sampling Methods:**
**1)** Sample too small, motorways not representative of average motorist, only done at one time of day and in one place. Better approach: Take samples from a range of different locations across the country, take samples at different times of day, have a much larger sample size, e.g. 1000.

**P.22 Questionnaires:**
**1) a)** This question is ambiguous. "A lot of television" can mean different things to different people.
**b)** This is a leading question, inviting the person to agree.
**c)** The answers to this question do not cover all possible options.

**P.23 Mean, Median, Mode and Range:**
First:  -14, -12, -5, -5, 0, 1, 3, 6, 7, 8, 10, 14, 18, 23, 25
Mean = 5.27, Median = 6, Mode = -5, Range = 39

**P.24 Quartiles and the Interquartile Range:**
**1) a)** 250 **b)** 750 **2)** 11 – 3 = 8

**P.26 Frequency Tables:**
Mean = 2.5, Median = 2,
Mode = 2, Range = 6

| No. of phones | 0 | 1 | 2 | 3 | 4 | 5 | 6 | TOTALS |
|---|---|---|---|---|---|---|---|---|
| Frequency | 1 | 25 | 53 | 34 | 22 | 5 | 1 | 141 |
| No. × Frequency | 0 | 25 | 106 | 102 | 88 | 25 | 6 | 352 |

**P.27 Grouped Frequency Tables:**

| Length L (cm) | 15.5≤L<16.5 | 16.5≤L<17.5 | 17.5≤L<18.5 | 18.5≤L<19.5 | TOTALS |
|---|---|---|---|---|---|
| Frequency | 12 | 18 | 23 | 8 | 61 |
| Mid-Interval Value | 16 | 17 | 18 | 19 | - |
| Freq × MIV | 192 | 306 | 414 | 152 | 1064 |

**1)** Mean = 17.4,
**2)** Modal Class = 17.5 ≤ L < 18.5
Median = 17.5 ≤ L < 18.5

**P.28 Cumulative Frequency:**
Median = 58, Lower Quartile = 53
Upper Quartile = 62,
Interquartile range = 9

| No of fish | 41 – 45 | 46 – 50 | 51 – 55 | 56 – 60 | 61 – 65 | 66 – 70 | 71 – 75 |
|---|---|---|---|---|---|---|---|
| Frequency | 2 | 7 | 17 | 25 | 19 | 8 | 2 |
| Cum. Freq. | 2 | 9 | 26 | 51 | 70 | 78 | 80 |

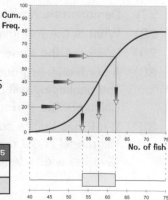

# <u>Answers</u>

**P.29 Histograms and Frequency Density:**
**1)**  0–5: 9,   5–10: 27,   10–15: 36,   15–20: 45,   20–25: 27,   25–35: 18,
35–55: 18,   55–65: 36,   65–80: 162,   80–90: 126,   90–100: 18

**2)**

```
0 | 3 6 7
1 | 1 2 3 4 6 7 9
2 | 0 2 4 6 6
```

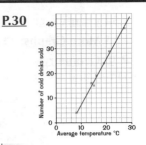

**P.30**

**P.30 Scatter Graphs and Bar Charts:**
**1) a)** and **b)** see graph, top right.   **1)**
**c)** Strong positive correlation.

**P.31 Spread of Data:**

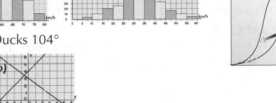

**2)**

**P.32 Other Graphs and Charts:**
**2)**  Stick insects 48°, Guinea Pigs 68°,  Rabbits  60°,  Ducks 104°

**P.33 Basic Algebra:  1) a)** +12  **b)** -6  **c)** x  **d)** -3
**2) a)** +18  **b)** -216  **c)** 2  **d)** -27  **e)** -336

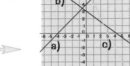

**P.35 Straight-Line Graphs:  1)**  -1.5

**P.36 Straight-Line Graphs:**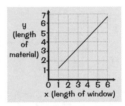

## *Revision Summary for Unit 1 — Part 1*

**2)**  £3710   **3)** £140.26   **4)**  240   **6)** Jill £18, Heather £15 and Susie £9   **7)** £17.33   **8)**  20 rolls   **12)** Yes

## *Revision Summary for Unit 1 — Part 2*

**8) a)** Mode and mean. **b)** Mode = size 6, Mean = 20 pairs   **11)**  $1 < m \le 5$.   **12)**  161 min
**17) a)** Both things increase or decrease together and they're closely related.  **b)** No

**21) a)** Yes.     **b)** E.g.

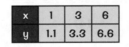

| x | 1 | 3 | 6 |
|---|---|---|---|
| y | 1.1 | 3.3 | 6.6 |

**22)** 2 cm³ / min

## *Unit 2*

**P.39 Types of Number:  1)**  Squares: 256, 289, 324, 361, 400     Cubes: 1331,  1728,  2197,  2744,  3375
Powers of 2:  64, 128, 256, 512, 1024
Powers of 10:  1000 000,  10 000 000,  100 000 000,  1 000 000 000,  10 000 000 000     Primes:  47,  53,  59,  61,  67

**P.40 Types of Number — Prime Numbers:  1)** 2, 3, 5, 7, 11, 13, 17, 19, 23, 29, 31, 37, 41, 43, 47
**2)** 101, 103, 107, 109

**P.41 Multiples, Factors and Prime Factors:  1)**  7, 14, 21, 28, 35, 42, 49, 56, 63, 70
**2)**  1, 2, 3, 4, 6, 9, 12, 18, 36 ;   1, 2, 3, 4, 6, 7, 12, 14, 21, 28, 42, 84
**3) a)**  990 = 2 × 3 × 3 × 5 × 11   **b)** 160 = 2 × 2 × 2 × 2 × 2 × 5

**P.42 LCM and HCF:   1)**  8, 16, 24, 32, 40, 48, 56, 64, 72, 80 and 9, 18, 27, 36, 45, 54, 63, 72, 81, 90  LCM = 72
**2)**  1, 2, 4, 7, 8, 14, 28, 56 and 1, 2, 4, 8, 13, 26, 52, 104    HCF = 8     **3)** 63     **4)** 12

**P.43 Powers and Roots:  1) a)** $3^8$ **b)** 4 **c)** $8^{12}$ **d)** 1 **e)** $7^6$   **2) a)** 64  **b)** 1/625  **c)** 1/5  **d)** 2  **e)** 125

**P.45 Fractions and Decimals:  1)** 1/7   **2) a)** terminating **b)** recurring **c)** terminating

**P.46 Fractions and Decimals:  1) a)** 5/32  **b)** 32/35  **c)** 23/20  **d)** 1/40  **e)** 167/27   **2) a)** 220  **b)**  £1.75

**P.47 Manipulating Surds and Use of π:**   **1)** $4\sqrt{2}$   **2)** $1 + 2\sqrt{2}$

**P.49 More Algebra:  1)** 4x + y – 4   **2)** $6p^2q – 8pq^3$
**3)** $8g^2 + 16g – 10$   **4)** $7xy^2(2xy + 3 – 5x^2y^2)$   **5)** $c^4/6d^3$   **6)** $\dfrac{2(17g − 6)}{5(3g − 4)}$

**P.51 Factorising Quadratics:   1 a)** x = 3 or -8   **b)**  x = 7 or -1   **c)**  x = 1 or -7   **d)**  x = 4 or -3/5

**P.52 Sequences:   1 a)** 20, 27, "Add 1 extra each time to the previous term."
**b)**  2000, 20 000, "Multiply the previous term by 10."   **c)**  4, 2, "Divide the previous term by 2."   **2)** 2n + 5

**P.53 Z Coordinates and Line Segments:   1)** (3, 5)   **2)** (5, 1)

# Answers

**P.54 y = mx + c:** **1)**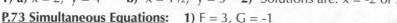

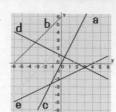 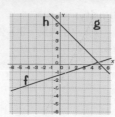

**P.55 More Graphs:** **1)** 0.5 km/h

**P.58 Geometry:**
**1)** 68° and 44°, or both 56° **2)** x = 66°

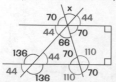

**P.59 Polygons:** **1)** Regular pentagon, 72°, 108° 12-sided regular polygon, 30°, 150°
**2)** 15 sides **3)** Pentagon, all the angles are either 36°, 72° or 108°    Octagon as shown →

**P.60 Symmetry and Circles:**
**1)**  H: 2 lines of symmetry, Rot$^{nl}$. symmetry Order 2,  N: 0 lines of symmetry, Rot$^{nl}$. symmetry Order 2
  E: 1 line of symmetry,  no Rotational symmetry,  Y:  1 line of symmetry,  no Rot$^{nl}$. symmetry
  M: 1 line of symmetry,  no Rotational symmetry,  S: 0 lines of symmetry, Rot$^{nl}$. symmetry Order 2,
  T:  1 line of symmetry, no Rot$^{nl}$. symmetry

**P.61 Areas and Nets:** **1)** 12 cm$^2$ **2)** 12 m$^2$ **3)** 21 m$^2$ **4)** 78 cm$^2$

**P.62 Volume and Projections:** **2) a)** (Trapezium) prism, V = 148.5 cm$^3$

**P.63 Metric and Imperial Units:** **1)** 13.5 litres **2)** 15 cm **3)** £1.00 per litre **4)** 80 km/h

**P.64 Speed, Distance and Time:** **1)** 1 hr 30 mins **2)** 3.15 km = 3150 m

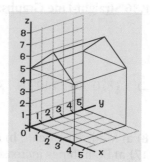

## Revision Summary for Unit 2 — Part 1

**6) a)** Approximately 2$^9$ **b)** Approximately 2$^{12}$ **7) a)** 9.7 × 10$^5$ **b)** 6.83 × 10$^6$
**c)** 3.56 × 10$^9$ **8)** 0.00000275 **21) a)** 10 m by 8 m **b)**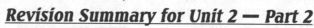

## Revision Summary for Unit 2 — Part 2

**8)** £420 **13)** 30 **14)**
**16)** £20

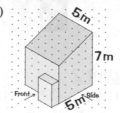

## Unit 3

**P.66 Calculating with Standard Index Form:** **1)** 8.54 × 10$^5$ ; 1.8 × 10$^{-4}$ **2)** 0.00456 ; 270 000
**3)a)** 2 × 10$^{11}$ **b)** 1 × 10$^8$

**P.67 Proportion and Variation:** **1) a)** E.g. Total cost vs No.of tins of Bone-tingling Fireball Soup
**b)** E.g. no. of people working on a job vs time taken to complete it.

**P.68 Proportion and Variation:** **1)** 0.632 Hz  40.8 cm

**P.69 Percentage and Proportion Change:** **1)** £20 500 **2)** £19.68

**P.70 Bounds and Reciprocals:** **1 a)** x — lower bound 2.315 m, upper bound 2.325 m
y — lower bound 0.445 m, upper bound 0.455 m **b)** max value of z = 4.57, min value of z = 4.51

**P.71 Solving Equations:** **1)a)** x = 2 **b)** x = -0.2 or -1/5 **c)** x = ±3

**P.72 Simultaneous Equations and Graphs:**
**1) a)** x = 2, y = 4 **b)** x = 1½, y = 3 **2)** Solutions are: x = -2 or x = 1.5

**P.73 Simultaneous Equations:** **1)** F = 3, G = -1

**P.74 Simultaneous Equations:**
**a)** f = 4 & g = 0 OR f = 40 & g = 6 **b)** f = -5/3 & g = -2/3 OR  f = 72 & g = 5
**c)** f = 9 & g = -3/2 OR f = 1 & g = 1/2 **d)** f = -3 & g = 33 OR f = 1/4 & g = -11/4

**P.75 The Quadratic Formula:** **1) a)** x = 0.39 or -10.39 **b)** x = 1.46 or -0.46 **c)** x = 0.44 or -3.44

**P.76 Completing the Square:** **1) a)** x = 0.39 or -10.39 **b)** x = 1.46 or -0.46 **c)** x = 0.44 or -3.44

**P.77 Rearranging Formulas:** **1)** C = 5(F − 32)/9 **2) a)** p = -4y/3 **b)** p = rq/(r + q) **c)** p = ±√{rq/(r + q)}

**P.78 Inequalities:** **1)** −2 ≤ x **2) a)** -6, -5, -4, -3, -2, -1, 0, 1, 2, 3, 4, 5, 6 **b)** -4, -3, -2, -1, 0, 1, 2, 3, 4

# Answers

**P.79 Inequalities:** **1)**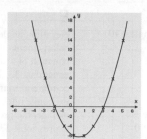

**P.80 Trial and Improvement:** **1)** x = 2.4

**P.81 Quadratic Graphs:**
**1)** See graph to the right.
Using graph, solutions are x = -2 and x = 3.

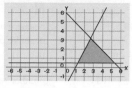

**P.83 Some Harder Graphs to Learn:** **1)a)** $x^2$ bucket shape
**b)** $-x^3$ wiggle (top left to bottom right) **c)** +ve inverse proportion graph
**d)** circle about origin, radius 6 **e)** –ve inverse proportion graph
**f)** $+x^3$ wiggle (bottom left to top right) **g)** $-x^2$ upside down bucket shape
**h)** $k^x$ curve upwards through (0,1)

**P.85 Graphs: Shifts and Stretches:**

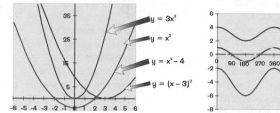

**P.87 Pythagoras' Theorem and Bearings:** **1)** BC = 8m **2)** 298° **3)** 118°

**P.88 Pythagoras, Lines and Line Segments:** **1)** 5 units
**2)** A line continues to infinity, whereas a segment is part of a line.

**P.90 Trigonometry — Sin, Cos, Tan:** **1)** x = 26.5 m **2)** 23.6° **3)** 32.6° (both)

**P.91 3D Pythagoras and Trigonometry:** **1)** 25.1° **2)** 7.07 cm

**P.93 The Sine and Cosine Rules:** **2)** 17.13m, 68.8°, 41.2°

**P.95 Vectors:** **1) a)** $-\mathbf{m} - \mathbf{b}$ **b)** $\frac{1}{2}\mathbf{b} - \frac{1}{2}\mathbf{a} + \mathbf{m}$ ($=\frac{1}{2}$AC)
**c)** $\frac{1}{2}(\mathbf{a} - \mathbf{b}) + \mathbf{m}$ **d)** $\frac{1}{2}(\mathbf{b} - \mathbf{a})$

**P.96 "Real Life" Vector Questions:**
Resultant Force: R = 21800 N, θ = 3.4°

**P.97 The Four Transformations:** **1) A→B** Rotation of 90° clockwise about the origin,
**B→C** Reflection in the line y = x, **C→A** Reflection in the y-axis, **A→D** Translation of $\begin{pmatrix} -9 \\ -7 \end{pmatrix}$

**P.98 The Four Transformations:**
**1)** **C→D**, Reflection in the y-axis, and an enlargement SF 2, centre the origin
**D→C**, Reflection in the y-axis, and an enlargement SF ½, centre the origin.
**2)** **A′→B**, Rotation of 180° clockwise or anticlockwise about the point (0,3).

**P.102 Circles, Cylinders and Spheres:** **1)** Perimeter 27.5 cm, area 35 cm²

**P.103 Circles, Cylinders and Spheres:** **1)** Cone, 20.3 m³ **2)** 33.5 cm³, 179.6 cm³

## *Revision Summary for Unit 3 — Part 1*

**4)** £9.99 **8) a)** 4.20 = 6x + 3y, 5.32 = 10x + 2y **b)** £6.72

## *Revision Summary for Unit 3 — Part 2*

**3)** 4.72 m **8)** 41° **30)** 213.63 cm² **31)** 150 cm wide, 300 cm long, 250 cm high.

# *Index*